"I should go back now to St. Clare's."

Iris was insistent. "I don't really belong here."

Zonar's hands closed on her shoulders and he searched her face with his dark eyes. "Is that what you've been doing all afternoon? Going around in circles trying to convince yourself that you should run away from me?"

"From you?" Iris stared back at him, knowing what her senses wanted. "Anyway, why should you care? You have your women. Please let me go away—just let me go!"

"I'm well aware that I could have other women," Zonar replied. "But you—you are strange, reserved, intriguing. I'm not allowing you to go back to that house of dry bones and good deeds, and deny yourself this...." His strong arms encircled her and his lips took hers....

Other titles by

VIOLET WINSPEAR

IN HARLEQUIN PRESENTS

THE SUN TOWER 178
LOVE IN A STRANGER'S ARMS 214
THE PASSIONATE SINNER 222
THE LOVE BATTLE 226
TIME OF THE TEMPTRESS 230
THE LOVED AND THE FEARED 238
THE AWAKENING OF ALICE 246
THE VALDEZ MARRIAGE 288
DESIRE HAS NO MERCY 300
THE SHEIK'S CAPTIVE 324

Other titles by

VIOLET WINSPEAR

IN HARLEQUIN ROMANCES

THE DANGEROUS DELIGHT 1344
BLUE JASMINE 1399
THE CAZALET BRIDE 1434
BELOVED CASTAWAY 1472
THE CASTLE OF THE SEVEN LILACS . 1514
RAINTREE VALLEY 1555
BLACK DOUGLAS 1580
THE PAGAN ISLAND 1616
THE SILVER SLAVE 1637
DEAR PURITAN 1658
RAPTURE OF THE DESERT 1680

VIOLET WINSPEAR

love is the honey

Harlequin Books

TORONTO • LONDON • NEW YORK • AMSTERDAM
SYDNEY • HAMBURG • PARIS • STOCKHOLM

Harlequin Presents edition published April 1980
ISBN 0-373-10354-9

Original hardcover edition published in 1980
by Mills & Boon Limited

Printed in U.S.A.

CHAPTER ONE

IRIS had never been inside a limousine before and she felt overawed by the comfort and luxury of the interior. There was walnut panelling, seats upholstered in soft leather, and a sliding glass panel that separated the passengers from the uniformed driver.

Unbelievably here she was, in the silver-grey car and on the verge of being driven all the way to the West Coast, and in her charge was the young son of a man named Zonar Mavrakis.

With Greek respect for Catholic education he had approached the Mother Superior of St Clare's and asked to employ a young woman to take care of his son for the summer. He expected to be in England for three months and wanted Aleko with him. He wished to hire someone English so Aleko could benefit by speaking the language daily.

Reverend Mother had produced Iris for his inspection; clad in the convent uniform she had looked suitably neat and unobtrusive, and after looking her over he had said that she would suffice. Iris had lived at St Clare's all her life, and she found the Greek so alarmingly foreign that she had felt like retorting that she wasn't sure she fancied him as an employer. But respect and obedience had been drilled into her and she accepted the decision that she was to work for him.

For days after that brief interview in the Mother Superior's office the look of the man stayed in her mind.

The challenge in his bold gaze, the battle scars of big business etched into his features, the aura of tough command that surrounded him. To look into his eyes, she thought strangely, had been like a flight through darkness into realms her innocence couldn't even imagine.

She was informed by her Superior that he had taken charge of a large hotel on the coast of Devon and wished to stay in supervision for a while. He had leased a nearby villa for his own use and there she would reside with Aleko, his motherless son of seven years.

So he was a widower, this Greek who strode into St Clare's and took over her life.

'The Mavrakis family is a very respected one in Greece,' said the Mother Superior. 'They are people of position, and if I was at all doubtful of this man, my child, I would have refused his petition, but you are ready to see something of the outside world and in taking care of this child you will be making yourself useful. The prospect doesn't unnerve you, does it?'

Iris let her mind dwell on the father of the boy and she felt again a nervous flutter at the thought of him. She almost said as much, but Mother Superior was looking at her with such calm eyes that it would seem foolish to blurt out that the dark-faced Greek had made her feel acutely aware that she was a shy convent girl who in her eighteen years had talked only with the priests who came to St Clare's to take confession. The man's dark eyes had searched her face and seen how naïve she was ... the ideal companion for his son.

'You are bound to feel strange at first.' Mother Superior rose to her feet to escort Iris from the cloisters of the convent, the only home she had ever known. As they crossed the courtyard to the gate Iris clenched her fingers around the grip of her travelling bag and felt both a sense of excitement and trepidation. Beyond that gate lay a world unknown to her; a car waited there to sweep her away from the sheltering walls and the guidance of the nuns.

'These few months away from us will help you to make up your mind about the future.' The tall gate groaned as it was opened. 'You must be given the right to choose. As you are aware, Iris, I don't believe in applying pressure upon my girls—the will to take our vows must be there in the heart. Go and find the answer that will either bring you back to us, or set you on a path away from us.'

Iris shook hands with the Mother Superior; the chauffeur of the big car took her bag and stowed it away in a compartent at the back. Iris shivered in the early morning air while a small boy pressed his nose to the window as the car door was opened and she entered the warm interior. The door closed, and then the gate of the convent, and the child studied her with eyes as dark as his father's.

'You are not a nun,' he said, speaking English carefully. 'I thought you would be wearing a long black skirt and a wimple on your head.'

Iris smiled nervously. She was wearing a plain dark-blue coat and a beret set at an angle to reveal her short hair. 'I shan't wear the habit until I take my vows,' she explained. 'Are you very disappointed because I'm not wearing a wimple on my head?'

He considered the question, his dark-lashed eyes fixed upon her face, a pale oval in the frame of her pale blonde hair, her lips unpainted and vulnerable, her cheekbones raised above slight hollows that gave her a slightly hungry look.

'I think in one of those long skirts you wouldn't be able to play games on the beach,' Aleko decided. 'I like very much to play volleyball. Papa and I play it together and he makes me run all over the place until I am puffed out.'

Iris tried to imagine the tall Greek playing childish games and romping on the sands ... she couldn't quite picture it, but it made him seem less nerve-racking. Having raised this boy himself, he no doubt had a great affection for him and would probably show him a gentler side than he showed other people.

'Are they grim, the vows you take to become a nun?' Aleko drew his top lip between his teeth as he studied her, a look she returned with a slight smile.

'Not grim,' she replied, 'but profound, so that a person has to think seriously about them before taking them.'

'Until then you are allowed to come out of the convent?'

She nodded, settling back into her seat as the limousine purred uphill and drove away from the convent, leaving it quietly enclosed within its high walls in the dim morning light. Iris gazed from the rear window of the car until the bell-tower could no longer be seen. It was then that a feeling almost of panic overcame her, but she had to stifle it and try to face calmly the task that lay ahead of her.

This was the first time she had been entirely on her own, without the company of other girls and the guardian nuns. Now she had to rely upon her own initiative and prove to Reverend Mother that if she had the nerve to face an alien world, then she would have the courage to enter the Sisterhood of St Clare's.

Until she saw and experienced life in the outside

world, she would be uncertain about the sacrifices involved when a girl vowed to become a nun.

She had to meet and get to know people on the other side of the convent walls and discover for herself if she had faith enough to face a life in which mystical devotion took the place of physical love for a man.

Iris studied the little boy at her side, a small dark replica of the tall Greek who had projected such an air of masculine authority as he stood in Mother Superior's office and swept his eyes searchingly over Iris in her unflattering uniform. She recalled vividly the thick blackness of his hair peaked dead centre of his equally black eyebrows. She had noticed the dark mole low down on the left side of his lean hard jaw, and the way the sun of Greece had long since burned itself into his skin. When he spoke, when he said decisively: 'The young woman appears suitable for my purpose, Reverend Mother,' the deep foreign timbre of his voice had touched Iris's nerve centres and she had wanted, right then, to plead with Mother Superior not to place her in his hands, the right one gripping the hogskin driving gloves, the left one bearing two gold rings side by side . . . ostentation, she told herself, until she learned from Mother Superior that he was a widower who probably wore his wife's ring in memory of her.

A woman couldn't have a child unless she gave herself to a man. Iris was aware that certain rituals took place and her innocence was rather appalled when she imagined being in the arms of someone like Aleko's father, at the mercy of his hard lips and his demanding male passions. Her skin grew warm as she tried to suppress the image . . . in her entire life she had never met anyone who made her have such thoughts and she had an urge to cross herself, something she and the other girls always did when they passed the small cemetery at the rear of the convent.

There was a stone figure of a monk there, his head cowled and his hands concealed in the wide sleeves of his robe. There was a story about him, that he had died rather than give in to the wiles of a rich woman who tried to make him break his vows. She had spread lies about him and he had withdrawn into his cell and refused to eat or drink until she told the truth, but she had left the country instead and left the poor monk to his fate.

One of the girls had been cynical of the story and said that it was crazy to perish for a principle. 'He perished for his faith,' Iris protested. Colette had laughed at her and retorted that faith didn't feed your body, only your soul, and she would prefer to have sole cooked in butter with a mayonnaise sauce.

Colette had been amusing and just a little wicked in Iris's estimation, but when she left the convent to go and live with her divorced mother Iris had missed their conflicts and their rather offhand friendship. Sinner and saint, Colette had embodied the two of them. She had said that the very thought of taking vows of chastity gave her the creeps. 'I want to live my life to the full,' she declared. 'You can't do that if you cut men out of your life ... they're the spice of life and I want to find out what it feels like to be in love even if I get hurt finding out. Your trouble, Iris, is that you're basically insecure. You came to the convent so young that you don't remember what it feels like to be kissed and made a fuss of.'

As the big car swept Iris and the boy inevitably away from the environs of St Clare's she admitted to herself that she had a lot to learn about life and a few months away from the convent would prove or disprove her suitability for the Sisterhood.

'It will take us many hours to reach Papa's hotel,' the boy said all at once. 'We have to drive to London and pass the Houses of Parliament even before we are on our way. Isn't it exciting, and may I know what I'm to call you?'

'My name is Iris.' A smile crept into her eyes at the way Aleko edged along his seat until his young body was pressing against her.

'That's the name of a flower.'

'I know, but here in England girls are sometimes given flower names.'

'Is it because of your eyes?'

'My eyes?'

'Yes, they seem to be that sort of colour, don't they?'

'I—I've never thought about it, Aleko. Girls in convents aren't encouraged to be vain.'

'Do they say their prayers a lot?'

'Several times a day.'

'I say mine when I go to bed. Papa listens while I say them and then I kiss the picture of Mama which always stands on my night table. I have never lived in England before, but last year I stayed with Papa in Paris.'

'You must have enjoyed that very much,' Iris smiled. 'Did you go to the top of the Eiffel Tower while you were there?'

'*Ne.*' His dark eyes sparkled. 'It was much fun going up and up and when we reached the top we saw all over Paris. Have you never been there?'

Iris shook her head. 'I've heard that it's very beautiful from one of the girls who was a pupil at St Clare's. She's French and lives in an apartment there with her mother. She once invited me to go and stay with her, but I don't suppose I shall ever manage it.'

'Because you are to be a nun?' Aleko asked. 'Will you always have to stay behind the high walls of the convent?'

'Only to live, Aleko. I shall probably go to the local infirmary to help care for the sick and aged.'

'Then it will be fun taking care of me, eh?' He grinned, dug a hand into his pocket and produced a bag of sticky candies. He offered them and Iris took one and popped it into her mouth.

'How does a person say 'thank you' in Greek?' she asked him.

'You say *efharisto poli.* They are very good candies, *ne*?'

'Delicious, but are you allowed to eat many?'

He shook his head. 'Papa says that candy will spoil my teeth, but Achille who drives the car allowed me to buy them. Papa has very fine teeth, you know, but that is because when he was a boy he and his brothers were so poor they couldn't afford to buy candy and used to go hunting for the spoiled *peponi* the stallholders had thrown away at the end of the day. Or they might be lucky and a fisherman might give them some of his octopus. They had no papa and Theos Lion was their *patir*. He's a very big man in Greece, *thespoinis,* and very rich now. His wife is from England and she has the most beautiful smile. I like so much to see her smile, but it is sad because she has no children and so I play in her big garden when I go to Petaloudes with Papa to see her. It is an island and there are so many butterflies you would not believe it. I like to go there and to go sailing in the big black *caique* which belongs to my uncle. He is so tall and when he lifts me to his shoulder it is like flying.

'I wish,' the boy sighed, 'I do wish Papa had a lady like Fenella.'

'Is Fenella your uncle's wife, Aleko?'

The boy nodded and crunched his candy. 'She's very kind and I know Papa likes her from the way he looks at her. Did your mother die when you were a baby, *thespoinis?*'

Iris nodded, for a child of seven years wouldn't understand the real truth, that one late afternoon eighteen years ago a local woman had brought her to St Clare's. Her mother had vanished from the woman's lodging house without a word of explanation, taking her few belongings with her but leaving the baby behind. After police enquiries had failed to trace her mother, Iris had been adopted into the convent and officially given the surname of Ardath, which had been the name her mother had been living under.

As Iris grew up she felt that the name had been invented by her mother in order to hide her true identity. Who she was and where she came from remained a mystery, but Iris inevitably grew up feeling that she was the child of careless, irresponsible passion—it didn't embitter her exactly, but it instilled in her a suspicion of men. She felt she wanted an armour against them, and the robes of a nun would provide it. No man would ever speak to her of love, and then leave her to do what her mother had done.

'I was lucky,' Aleko found her hand with his sticky one, 'I had a Papa to take care of me. What became of yours?'

'He—he went away and never came back, Aleko.'

'And so you lived with the nuns?'

'Yes. They're very kind.' Kind, she thought, but always just a little distant so that sometimes she wondered what it felt like to be cuddled up close to someone who wanted to kiss and make a fuss of her. She had never known that kind of affection, though she had always been fed and clothed and well educated. If a girl grew up an orphan at St Clare's it was assumed that she'd enter the order when she came of age. Iris had never rebelled against this, no more than she had against the rosaries, the hymns and hours of devotional silence. She had never known anything else but the ambience of the convent, its stained glass windows and the pealing of bells in the narrow tower. The nuns in their wide-sleeved habits and white-lined headrobes that somehow made them mystical. The sanctuary of St Clare's had taken the place of the warm rough and tumble of life enjoyed by girls who had a family.

For Iris it was a case of what she had never known she had never greatly missed, and she knew from her friend Colette that home life wasn't always perfect. Colette's parents had battled through eight years of stormy marriage until they had finally divorced, and Iris was inclined to wonder if love between a man and a woman could ever be the magical thing the romantic poets wrote about. Two people meeting as if fated to do so, falling so deeply in love that only by being together could they ever find contentment.

It was just a myth, she told herself. Just a fiction dreamed up by writers in order to sell dreams to people. Dreams vanished the moment you opened your eyes to the morning light and it was better not to believe that they ever came true.

By the time the car was travelling along beside the Embankment in London the morning light was spreading over the spires of Westminster and gleaming on the water of the Thames. Aleko craned eagerly forward in order not to miss anything. He was full of chatter and seemed not to possess the initial shyness of English children. The Thames was not like the Seine, he told her, and wasn't it peculiar that rivers were so different when they were all made up of water.

'It's probably the buildings alongside them that make them seem unalike,' she said, and like the child she was filled with the wonder of London at this time of the day. It had a kind of beauty that later on would be disturbed by the passage of heavy traffic and the smear of engine fumes, but right now it had a haunting kind of magic, a mixture of the old and the new mingling together in the smudged light to create a canvas she would hang in her mind as a reminder of this unexpected journey to the West Coast, to act as governess to a little Greek boy while his father supervised the initial take-over of the Monarch Hotel which the Mavrakis Company had added to its chain of business concerns.

Iris had already learned from Aleko that the Mavrakis clan owned hotels in the major cities and were bosses of Sunline Air and Seaways. Altogether a successful and expanding corporation; a fact which increased her nervousness of Zonar Mavrakis, who no doubt kept his son with him a great deal in order to instil into him a feeling for high finance. The Mavrakis brothers had come a long way since the days when bruised watermelon or a piece of octopus were considered a luxury.

Around noon Achille the driver pulled into the driveway of a roadside restaurant and they went inside to make themselves comfortable and to eat lunch. Achille took charge, to Iris's relief. It probably came naturally to the Greek male, she supposed, to take control of any situation. He ordered steak, chips and tomatoes for the three of them. *Ne,* Aleko could have lemonade with his lunch, but would the *thespoinis* join in him in a glass of lager?

'I'd like to,' she smiled. 'I've never had it in my life. Is it nice?'

'Nice like many things a girl never has until a man makes the offer.' His eyes looked into hers, dark as the moustache across his upper lip and the sideburns that followed the slopes of his foreign face. Iris, who had lived among nuns all her life, felt confused by him. She wanted to be friends with the other employees of Zonar Mavrakis, but she shrank from the idea of being flirted with.

'At the convent,' she said, 'we drink water with our meals, so I mustn't get a taste for lager, must I?'

'You are now miles away from the convent,' Achille said meaningfully.

'But I shall be going back at the end of the summer,' she replied, 'to take my own vows.'

'You go back for that?' he exclaimed. His eyes flashed over her. 'It is a hard step for a girl to take—what happens if you get a taste for things other than lager while you are out in the world?'

'What things?' She asked the naïve question before she could stop herself.

'The things girls naturally like. Dresses, make-up, and going to a dance or to the cinema with a man.' He looked her over from her flat-heeled shoes to her beret. 'It isn't a crime, you know. Life is for the living.'

'I know what I want to do with my life,' she rejoined.

'One so young?'. He stroked a finger against his moustache and stared at her. Aleko sat there at the table watching the exchange with a great deal of interest, his lips around the straw in his lemonade.

'Life, *thespoinis*, has strange ways of its own and we Greeks have a saying that no woman should live like a fruitless fig tree.'

'I'm English, thank you, and I shall live the way it suits me!'

'Have you always been at the convent?' he wanted to know.

'Yes——'

'Then it will make quite a change for you, eh, being away from all that piety?'

'You're being rather impudent, and if you don't mind we'll change the subject.'

'Will you tell the boss that I've rattled you?' A smile quirked his moustache and he glanced at Aleko. 'You don't want a stiff-skirt for a governess, do you? Your *patir* likes his glass of wine and his women, does he not?'

'That's no way to talk to a child!' Iris exclaimed.

'Have I shocked you?' Achille mocked. 'Aleko knows well enough that his father isn't a saint but a man. A man, *thespoinis*.' The chauffeur leaned across the table until Iris could see herself in his bold eyes. 'You don't know much about men, do you? Would you like me for your teacher?'

'No, thank you!' Iris looked scornful. 'I can assure you that no aspects of my education have been that neglected. I can do without the kind of lessons you have in mind.'

'You might get bored being with a child all the time. I could show you a bit of life while you have the chance to see it.'

'I've been hired to take care of Aleko and I expect

we'll find plenty to amuse us at Tormont.'

'Paddling in the rock pools and building sand castles?'

'Yes, anything that will amuse Aleko. That's what I'm being paid for.'

'So you're the selfless type, eh?' He leaned back in his chair and laughed to himself. 'Whatever will the boss make of you? I don't think he has much use for little prudes like you.'

'I'm not for his use,' she said smartly. 'And now shall we eat lunch so we can be on our way? We don't want to spend all day getting to Tormont, do we?'

'A proper little madam, aren't you?' Achille cocked an eyebrow at Aleko. 'What do you make of this vinegar puss of a governess your *patir* has picked out for you?'

'She's nice to me.' Aleko sucked the last of his lemonade up through the straw. 'You think all the girls like you in your uniform and leather boots, Achille, but Miss Iris is to be a nun and they mustn't have anything to do with men.'

'Is that so, young one?' Achille shot a grin at Iris. 'He's a bright boy, isn't he? That's what comes of travelling around with his father and meeting some of his father's girl-friends. Do you remember the one in Paris, young one? She was a real stunner, wasn't she? Long brown hair, hazel eyes, and not much older than your Miss Iris. Really gone on the boss, eh? You nearly had a new mother, didn't you, but the boss is wily. He likes his freedom too much and the sea's too full of fish to make a meal out of one little catch. All the same she was quite a girl. Had what we Greeks call charisma. Do you know what that means, little governess?'

'It means someone who makes magic.'

'Ne.' Achille cut vigorously into his steak and forked

a chunk of it into his mouth. He chewed and watched Iris. 'The *kyrios* won't know you're alive, do you know that? Maybe you were hoping to catch his eye, but he has the tastes of a rich man and he goes for champagne girls, and you've never even tasted lager. Go on, taste it.'

Iris picked up the slender glass of pale gold lager and sipped it. She found it slightly bitter, but was unsurprised by what Achille told her about Zonar Mavrakis. She had summed him up herself as the conquering type who would regard charming women as prizes for successful endeavour. Iris lived under no illusion that she had appealed to his expensive tastes; she came under the heading of plain and serviceable and unlikely to cause him problems as summer governess for his son.

'What do you think of the lager?' Achille asked her.

'It's all right,' she said, 'but I don't think I'm likely to develop a crush on it.'

'Expecting the boss to give you champagne?' he mocked sarcastically.

'No,' she replied. 'I don't imagine it's a great deal different from lager.'

'You just try a glass or two and find out the difference! It would soon turn your head, and maybe melt some of the ice in your veins. You should see Athens and drink *ouzo* while the men dance to *bouzouki* music, that would liven you up, Miss Iris.'

Iris decided that the best way to deal with Achille was to ignore him. He probably thought himself a lady-killer in his smart uniform and the leather boots that hugged the calves of his legs, and he had to prove to himself that he could also turn the head of a girl out of a convent. She gave all her attention to Aleko and was relieved when they were back in the car and proceeding on the last lap of their journey. Full up with lunch, the boy became drowsy and fell off to sleep in the crook of her arm. She studied his young face and the long lashes that curtained his eyes as he slept.

Being in charge of the child still felt strange to her and she wondered what the next few weeks held in store for her. It would all seem very bewildering at first; she would miss the routine she was used to and would have to adapt herself to the ways of a stranger's household.

In Aleko's young features she saw traces of the father; that man whose inner fabric had to be very tough indeed. Men didn't become business potentates unless they had nerves of iron, subtle brains, and a body that could withstand a lot of gruelling pressure.

Zonar Mavrakis had seemed to her a very big man because she was accustomed to seeing only the learned and rather elderly priests who came to the convent. She had noticed his strong, flexible-looking shoulders, his assured bearing and worldly manner ... his gaze that dominated a woman. It hadn't taken him any time at all to get around Mother Superior, a woman of firm character whom none of the Sisters or girls ever thought of disobeying. Only Colette had ever been pert to her and had got away with it because she was so pretty that people indulged her as they might a saucy and beguiling little cat.

Iris had wanted to disobey Mother Superior when she had stood there and the big Greek had looked her over as if she were an object on a stall that he could afford to purchase. She remembered that he wore a charcoal pinstripe, a light grey shirt and a knitted silk tie. Fine costly materials that fitted him like a tailored glove. He could afford whatever he wished and had taken it into his head to add an English governess to his household for the summer.

Iris hoped that so long as she took good care of his son he would hardly notice her. Seven years seemed a long time for such a vigorous-looking man to remain a widower; Iris had heard that Greek woman rarely remarried after losing a husband ... did the men of that country follow the same rule? Or did it suit Zonar Mavrakis to take his pleasures where he found them?

A tide of warmth crept over Iris's skin. She didn't usually have these kind of thoughts about people and supposed it had something to do with being released from the restrained atmosphere of St Clare's. Whether or not the man noticed her, she would be living under his roof, a girl who had always lived among women who had taken vows of chastity.

Aleko stirred and pressed closer to her, pushing his boyish head against her breast. Iris drew her lip between her teeth ... physical contacts had been discouraged at the convent and no one had ever been this close to her before.

This boy who lay in the circle of her arm was the son of a man whose commanding looks made her feel very unsure of herself. He might find it easy enough to ignore her presence at the villa, but Iris had an uneasy feeling that she wasn't going to find it a tranquil experience living in the same house with him. He was too large and masculine; too boldly defined as a person not to intrude upon her imagination, but it was now a little too late to wish she had nerved herself and refused to be employed by him.

She and Aleko were friends already, but she fervently wished that he had a less disturbing man for a father.

The boy stirred partly awake and gazed up at her with his Greek eyes. 'Are we nearly there?' he yawned.

Iris glanced from the car window and saw palm trees set along a road that arched towards ochre cliffs and a deep blue sky. Her heart skipped a beat ... yes, they were almost there! Soon they would arrive at the villa!

CHAPTER TWO

THE limousine rolled smoothly uphill, affording breathtaking views of the wide blue bay of Tormont, above which the Monarch Hotel was situated. They had to pass the hotel on their way to the villa, and Iris saw with wonderment the size of the place. It was white-stoned and built in tiers like a Florentine palace, with balconies in front of the windows. At its entrance stood a uniformed doorman wearing white gloves. Several smart cars were parked in the driveway, and the building itself was surrounded by gardens that wended their way up and down the red cliffs. Palm trees and tamarisks gave the place a Mediterranean air, and there was a green stretch of golfing links patched by sandbanks.

'That's Papa's hotel,' Aleko said eagerly. 'Is it not grand?'

'Very grand indeed,' Iris agreed. 'I like the way its gardens stretch down to the seashore.'

No wonder Zonar Mavrakis wished to supervise the running of the place for a while! It was obviously the kind of hotel that catered for people with money, one of those five-star places, with swimming pools inside and out, a couple of ballrooms, gracious lounges, a resident pianist, and tea at four o'clock served by waitresses. Iris had read a book of Arnold Bennett's in which such an hotel had been described; the schoolroom at the convent had been stocked with books by certain of the classical writers, also including Galsworthy, and she was acquainted with the Forsytes and could imagine that modern equivalents of them stayed at the Monarch.

Their car proceeded on its way up the winding hillside and the views of the sea became even more spectacular. Iris had never seen water so deeply blue, with a thick lacy surf that creamed in against the shingle and the rocks. Some of the rocks stood like great boulders in the sea, upon which groups of seagulls were perched.

Achille turned the car around a steep bend and there, standing in a large space scooped out of the cliffs, was the Villa Circe.

It seemed unbelievable to Iris, who had lived all her life in the rather dour atmosphere of St Clare's, that for the next few months she would be living in a place as picturesque as the villa. When she stepped from the car in the halfmoon driveway all she could do was stand and feast her eyes on the place, the left wing being two-storied with balconies and arched entrances, then came a circular central portion under a peaked roof. The right-hand wing was one-storied and rambling, with windows and doors in varying sizes. The entire building had crusty white walls and rust-red tiling. Its terraced gardens sloped in a dizzy way to the sea and were vivid with clumps of rockery plants. Above and around the villa were those hanging cliffs of redstone.

It was like a painting come to life and Iris caught her breath in wonderment. She hadn't known all these years that there were houses like this one, and people fortunate enough to live in them. Riches had seemed to her no more than fiction, but it had to be remembered that the Greek brothers who could afford this kind of gracious living had worked tenaciously hard for it, using brawn and brain to acquire their money. As children they had often gone without a meal, and Zonar Mavrakis had not been dressed as his little boy was, in a kidskin coat with a woolly collar.

Iris turned to look at him, standing there beside the big car as Achille took the luggage from the trunk. The boy was stroking the mascot on the powerful hood of the limousine, a silver lady in a flying cloak.

He grinned at her. 'Your eyes look ever so big,' he remarked.

'It makes a change for your governess,' said Achille, 'finding out that beyond the grim high walls of her convent the sea is blue and the air can stroke your skin like silk. She's too accustomed to the hair shirt.'

'Do you wear one of those, Miss Iris?' the boy enquired curiously.

Achille gave a roar of laughter as he mounted the villa steps with the luggage. 'He's a caution, isn't he? He's only known his father's young women and they wear lace on their shifts.'

'It isn't right for you to talk the way you do,' Iris chided him. 'I'm sure Mr Mavrakis wouldn't care for it in front of Aleko.'

'Going to tell on me?' Achille mocked her, pressing a hard brown thumb to the bell set into the wall at the side of the arching front door. There were tubs of flowering plants at either side of the door, and the air that came off the surface of the sea did seem to brush Iris's face and neck with a touch of silk. Suddenly she felt prim and drab in her dark-blue coat, and intensely aware of how different she must look compared to the young women who usually stepped from the big car owned by Zonar Mavrakis. She hadn't their charm, and wore plain cotton under her blouse and skirt. When the front door of the villa was opened by a maid, Iris stumbled over the brass-bound step instead of walking in composedly.

'It's that lager,' Achille grinned. 'It's gone to your head.'

The maid seemed to take this remark seriously and she gave Iris a disapproving look. 'If you will come this way, miss, I'll show you where you are to sleep.'

'May I come as well?' Achille drawled. 'To bring the luggage.'

The maid said something to him, but Iris hardly heard. She was too busy looking around the hall, where at the far end there were lacy iron doors opening on to a sun-terrace where she could see a suite of cane furniture. As they crossed to the staircase she noticed that the floor was tiled, very small tiles forming a kind of mosaic. She studied it and realised it was an occult symbol, of the sun and the moon meeting at the centre in a starburst.

She smiled a little to herself and drew her hand along the handrail of the stairs, smooth as black silk and sweeping up the side of the staircase that rose through the two levels of the villa, paintings upon the creamy walls of what she took to be Tormont scenery.

It was a fairly large villa and yet there was nothing cold about it. There was a warm gleam to the oaken floors, where here and there an oriental rug lay like a splash of colour. They walked beneath an archway of deep-red tiles along the gallery and the maid opened a door just beyond the arch. She glanced at Iris as she did so, giving her a rather inquisitive look that took in the modest quality of her clothes; it was a look which said without words that Iris had never slept in a bedroom like this one.

Indeed she hadn't, and she couldn't suppress a gasp. She had always shared a dormitory with other girls, and slept in a narrow bed completely covered by a serviceable bedspread. Sometimes in winter the girls shivered at night because the blankets were thin from their years of service, and on winter mornings the floors had felt hard and cold to bare feet. Some of the girls wore their stockings in bed, but Iris preferred to put hers on fresh in the morning.

Here in this high-ceilinged bedroom, set against wallpaper with huge flowers printed on it, was a wide bed with a brocaded headboard, draped to the carpet in matching brocade of a deep apricot. There were chairs whose arms curled round to hug cushions, and a dressing-table with porcelain lamps on it, a mirror-stand and powder bowls whose silver lids caught the sea-light through the long windows. A corner table held a cut-glass bowl of flowers, and on the night table stood another lamp, a small clock, and some books.

Aleko climbed on to the bed and watched Iris as she gazed around the room, clutching to her the old-fashioned handbag one of the Sisters had given her. All that was inside was a handkerchief, a purse and a comb. Iris had never owned face powder and she couldn't take her eyes off the silver-lidded bowls on the dressing-table, companioned by scent-bottles with the amber gleam of perfume through the glass.

'I——' Iris turned to the maid, 'I surely shan't be sleeping here. I think a much plainer room would be more suitable for me. I should prefer it——'

The maid looked at her as if she were daft. 'The *kyrios* gave orders you were to sleep here, miss. The housekeeper has had me polishing and putting things to rights all the morning. What's wrong with the room?'

'It's perfectly charming.' Iris flushed as she caught the flicker of scorn in the maid's eyes. 'I just didn't expect anything like this—I live in a convent, you see, and we don't go in for this kind of luxury. I could speak to the housekeeper myself about another room.'

'Are you afraid you'll get to like all this?' Achille looked around him. 'Consider yourself fortunate, Miss Iris. My rooms over the garage aren't half so stylish and comfortable. I wouldn't turn this down if I were you —you might annoy the boss.'

'Mr Mavrakis gave his orders,' the maid agreed. 'Right next door is the young master's bedroom— there's an adjoining balcony right over the sea. You ought to think yourself lucky, miss. I've worked for people who aren't all that considerate about where the governess sleeps.'

'I'm sure Mr Mavrakis means well——' Iris felt as if her cheeks were burning.

'He always means what he says!' The maid crossed the room to the adjoining door and flung it open to reveal a room similar to Iris's but with a small bed in it and an apple-green colour scheme. 'Tea will be served presently, miss, if you care to come down to the afternoon room.'

'Will there be cream slices?' Aleko bounced up and down on Iris's bed and she listened in vain for the tired protest of springs under a thinly stuffed mattress in which the flock collected into uncomfortable lumps.

'I'll tell Cook you want some,' the maid said. 'And do stop messing up that bed, there's a good boy. Look what you're doing to that cover!'

He rolled on it carelessly, and Iris decided that she'd better show the maid and the chauffeur that she wasn't quite the ninny they thought her. She walked over to Aleko, hustled him off the bed and straightened the cover—the feel of the silky brocade under her fingers making them tingle with a forbidden longing to stroke the silk.

'You must treat nice things with more respect, Aleko,' she said. 'They cost a lot of money.'

'Papa has lots of money,' he said carelessly. 'It's a nice big bed so I think I'll sleep in it with you. I sometimes sleep in Papa's bed and it's better than being on your own.'

'His father's boy,' Achille guffawed. Iris flung him a furious look.

'Aleko knows full well he's going to sleep in his own bed, and now if you don't mind I'll wash his face and hands before we come down to tea.'

'He's right,' Achille held her gaze with his bold one, 'it is better than being on your own.'

'Do you mind going?' She stood there giving him what she hoped was one of Sister Rachel's most freezing looks. That particular Sister had served in Africa where she had once subdued a village riot by out-staring the leader of it, who had threatened her with a machete. Achille merely smiled at Iris and then sauntered to the door, where he stood holding the handle a moment.

'If you feel like taking any excursion just let me know. The boy will be taking riding lessons at Honeyton Stables and it's a little too far for walking and there's a nice little pub up there where we could have a drink together. I'm at your disposal when the boss doesn't need me.'

'Very well,' she said. 'Thank you for letting me know about the riding lessons.'

'You are welcome, Miss Iris.' Achille was openly mocking her for her primness. 'He's also swimming with the pro at the hotel and learning ping-pong. I expect the boss will fill you in.' The chauffeur winked and closed the door behind him, but not before Iris heard him laugh and say something about her to the maid. Then they walked away and she stood silent a moment, feeling a tremor of nerves run through her. It would appear that she was going to have to face entering that grand hotel, and the very look of it had overawed her.

She took off her beret and unbuttoned her coat. 'Do you like horses, Aleko?' she asked, taking her coat across to the clothes closet, where a row of hangers waited to be hung with pretty dresses and smart suits. She had only one dress suitable for evening wear and that had long sleeves and a cowl neckline and was a rather drab shade of mauve. Sister Ruth had made her a couple of dresses for day wear, but apart from that she had only her brown skirt and three white blouses that all looked alike. Her shoes were flat-heeled and serviceable ... she had no idea what it felt like to wear stylish shoes with heels off the ground.

'Riding is fun.' Aleko came to her and stared into the clothes closet. 'It's very big, isn't it, Miss Iris?'

'Yes,' she sighed, 'far too large for my small assortment of clothes. I expect the people who stay at your father's hotel are very smart, especially the ladies.'

'And pretty, I expect.' He gazed up at her. 'With your hat off you have nice hair—it's the colour of caramel toffees. Can we go down to the hotel after we've had our tea so I can see Papa? He'll be there in charge of things.'

'I daresay he will,' she half smiled, and unaware she touched a hand to her hair, whose softness she had sometimes rather guiltily liked. Vanity was firmly repressed in the convent's pupils and there were very few mirrors at St. Clare's, certainly not a long one like that fixed inside the door of the clothes closet. It showed Iris to herself in a way that startled her; it showed her, for instance, that she had a slim, rather delicate outline, with a pale neck rising out of the prim collar of her blouse, and somehow a breakable look to the ankles which had to bear the weight of the black laced-up shoes that were totally charmless. If anyone had told Iris that she had lovely hands and skin, she would have been startled and confused.

Iris was a girl very much imbued with the spirit of St Clare's and it wasn't in her nature to think about herself. She gazed at her reflection as if looking at a stranger. Her skirt was about two inches longer than the length being worn by girls doing their shopping or walking their dogs whom she had studied from the windows of the car. They also wore their hair in a much more stylish way and she supposed she looked quaint compared to them.

'Shall we see about your hands and face?' she said to Aleko.

'I can wash myself,' he informed her.

'Voluntarily?' She went across and opened a door half-concealed in an angle of her room and there was a bathroom tiled from ceiling to floor in sea-blue. Iris gasped at the luxury of it, the deep wide tub, the pedestal hand-basin of patterned porcelain, with deep scoops for the soap, and the matching toilet and bidet. Underfoot was carpet, and never in her life had Iris seen carpet in a bathroom!

'Look, sea-horses,' Aleko was fiddling about with the taps of the wash-basin. 'Papa said this house was a nice one—do you like it, Miss Iris?'

'I—I can't quite believe that it's real.' She picked up a bar of translucent soap and sniffed its delicate perfume. 'You're a fortunate boy, Aleko, to have a father who can afford all this. I hope you're grateful to him?'

'Are you terribly poor?' Aleko rubbed soap on to a washcloth, introduced it fleetingly to his face and then dropped it into the water.

'That's no way to wash your face, young man.' Iris took charge of the proceedings. 'Money isn't everything, you know. There are a lot of other things in life, like helping other people, making things grow in a garden, listening to music. You musn't grow up confusing poverty of the pocket with poverty of the soul. A person can be rich without having money in the bank.'

'But it does buy lots of things.' Aleko held up his face to be dried and when he batted his wet clustering lashes Iris thought how endearing he looked and she had an impulse to hug him. Such impulses had not been encouraged or welcomed at the convent where restraint had been taught and instead she gave his cheek a little stroke.

'Now the hands, my boy.' He dipped the sticky things in the basin and she watched while he soaped them. 'I suppose you mean lots of candy and things to play with, not to mention riding lessons? I hope your father doesn't spoil you, Aleko?'

'He's very fond of me.' Aleko held out clean hands to be wiped. 'I'm not afraid of him, you know, but many people are—I have heard Achille say so. He says my papa is a very tough cookie.'

'Cookie?' Iris looked puzzled, for cinema slang was unknown to her.

'They say it in the films, Miss Iris. Achille takes me to the cinema sometimes and we eat popcorn and ice-cream. It's most enjoyable.'

'Doubtless, if you spend the afternoon filling yourself up with that kind of stuff. What sort of films do you see?'

'Those about bank robbery and sometimes a Western, and once we saw a very good film about a forest fire. That was superior!'

'Mmmm.' Iris studied her young charge as she groomed his dark silky hair with her comb. Nice-looking, she thought, with tracings of the father about the eyes but with an innocent charm which probably reflected the mother who had died so tragically. Yes, Zonar Mavrakis would spoil the boy to a certain extent, and also being a busy man he wouldn't always be on hand to safeguard him from influences such as Achille.

'Tell me something, Aleko, why does your father's driver speak the way he does? He sounds more English than Greek, yet he is a Greek, isn't he?'

Aleko nodded. 'He was born in London, but he has a Greek family. They live there, you see. His father has a café. Achille is a very superior driver and that's why Papa has him to drive the cars.'

'The cars?'

'We have four,' Aleko told her proudly. 'The Rolls limousine is the best, of course, and you should see Papa's racing model. Whew, can it go! Achille likes to drive it and Papa doesn't always know that he does so.'

'Achille takes rather a lot on himself, if you ask me.' Iris ran the water out of the wash-basin and wiped it around until it was shining again. Being tidy and neat was part of her; a clean home meant a clean heart, she had always been taught. She wondered if Zonar Mavrakis had chosen someone like her to take care of Aleko because he had grown a trifle worried about the boy?

'Achille is also a tough cookie.' The boy caught her by the hand and tugged her out of the bathroom. 'Let's go downstairs and have our tea. I'm starving!'

'You don't know the meaning of the word,' she half-smiled. They left her bedroom and went along the gallery to the stairs, where before she could restrain him Aleko climbed on the glossy stair-rail and slid all the way to the hall. Iris felt her heart give a thud. She didn't dare to think how she'd face the father if anything happened to Aleko while he was in her charge, but at the same time she realised that she couldn't restrain the child. He was healthy, active and adventurous, and she would have to pray that he kept that way during the time she was with him.

Now he was hopping about in the hall, jumping in and out of the tiled mosaic of the sun and the moon. When she reached him he grinned up at her. 'Did I scare you?' he asked, rather gleefully.

'Oh, I'm not a spoilsport,' she replied. 'But I hope you'll remember that if you come to any great harm your father will lay the blame on me. That wouldn't be kind, would it?'

'Achille says I'm tough as a tomcat,' Aleko confided. 'He says I take after my papa and Theos Lion. They are Spartans, you know. They are from that part of Greece.'

Iris's eyes glimmered a deep flower blue, though she was unaware of how exactly her eyes reflected the shadings of the iris. Hers was a smile of vagrant charm; a little shy, a little unsure.

'Strange,' she murmured. 'A Sister at the convent was always drumming it into us to be Spartans and face life as a battle and a challenge. I—I suppose that's what your father and his brothers have done.' Though, she added in her mind, they had probably striven for financial reasons; hers, when she took her vows, would be for spiritual ones.

The afternoon room was easy enough to find; they followed the maid in with the tea trolley. A different maid, Iris noticed, slightly older and with her lace cap set squarely on her head. She wheeled the trolley to a couch and Aleko ran over to inspect the stand of cakes and another holding small triangular sandwiches.

'Thank you.' Iris smiled at the maid and tried not to feel overwhelmed by all this grand living she was unaccustomed to. A silver teapot, she noticed, a matching milk jug and sugar bowl, and bone china teacups that could almost be seen through. She sank down on the couch, a girl who was used to hard-backed chairs and holding her spine straight against those hard backs.

'Have you everything you require, miss?'

'Oh, yes.' Such a pile of sandwiches and cakes would have fed a dozen girls at the convent. 'More than enough!'

'Very well, miss.' The tall door closed behind the maid and for the first time in her life Iris lifted a silver teapot and poured out the tea into the charming cups. Aleko helped himself to sandwiches and sat down on a big velvet hassock to eat them. Iris stirred her tea and let her eyes travel around the room ... she felt as if she were awake in a dream, for there was another velvet couch to match the one she sat on, masses of maize-coloured curtains at the long windows, the warm glow of mahogany furniture and a beautifully woven carpet.

She sipped her tea and gazed at the sun through the silk figured curtains, the translucent net blowing slightly in a breeze that carried the smell of the sea.

Had Reverend Mother been aware that she was coming to a house like this?

'Can I have a cream slice now?' Aleko asked.

'Have you eaten those sandwiches already?'

He came over to her and took a cake oozing with cream. 'Yes, do let's hurry. I want to see Papa.' He bit deep into the cake and fidgeted. 'Come on, aren't you going to eat anything? You just keep looking about the room.

'It's such a beautiful room, Aleko. We have nothing like it at the convent.'

He shrugged, a rather spoiled little boy whose father was a rich man. 'I want to go down to the hotel. I can find my own way——'

'That would look fine on my first day as your governess,' she interjected. 'You'll stay here while I have another cup of tea. Look, have one of these apple tarts and be patient. Patience is a virtue.'

The boy stared at her, his nostrils drawn in, and then with a grin he took the tart and nibbled round the edges of it. 'Aren't you hungry, Miss Iris?' he asked. 'Don't nuns eat a great deal of food?'

'They aren't self-indulgent, Aleko, and I'm not yet a nun. Do you want a drop more tea, or perhaps some milk?'

'Milk,' he decided. 'Can I drink it out of the jug?'

'Indeed not! Hand me your cup.'

'Are you a termagant?' he asked, handing over the cup.

'Now where did you hear a word like that?' She poured the milk and gave it to him.

'That's what Achille says about his sister, that she's a termagant and ought to have her bottom spanked.' Aleko's eyes gleamed with fun over the edge of his cup.

'That's what will happen to you if you play me up.' Iris warned. 'I'm here to see that you don't get into mischief while your father keeps busy at the hotel.'

'Do you expect you'll fall in love with him?'

'I—I beg your pardon?' Her eyes opened wide and startled; she couldn't believe that she'd heard correctly.

'Girls are always after Papa,' Aleko confided. 'I expect you'll be the same, won't you, or mustn't you fall in love because you're going to be a nun?'

'I most certainly have no intention of—the very idea!' An image of the big graceful Greek strode through her mind, his black hair tapering into sideburns along each side of his lean jaw, his eyes compelling above the bold Grecian nose. Holy heaven, why couldn't Aleko have had a small tame man for a father instead of an intimidating tycoon who treated girls like playthings!

'You are never to say such a thing ever again, Aleko,' she said reprovingly. 'It's disrespectful to your father and me. I'm his employee, not some silly idle girl with nothing better to do than chase your father for his money.'

'The girl in Paris was most pretty,' he mused. 'She was up on the Eiffel Tower when we went there and she started talking to Papa; she had long hair and it was blowing in the wind. I could see she liked Papa.'

'And what about him?' Iris couldn't help feeling curious. 'Did he like her?'

He nodded, and then said thoughtfully: 'But not, I think, as he likes Fenella. When he speaks with her when we go to Petaloudes his voice is all deep and soft.'

'Is your uncle's wife pretty?' Iris asked; she could feel inside her a mounting interest in the Mavrakis clan and this island of butterflies where the eldest brother and his English wife resided. Lion was a strong, unusual name, probably shortened from a long Greek name. Zonar also had a Greek strength about it, and something occult. Spartan brothers to whom success and women were drawn like moths to a lamp.

'Fenella is beautiful.' Aleko knelt upon the hassock and blinked his long eyelashes. 'Papa says so. He says she is quiet and beautiful like a butterfly, but Theos Dimi's wife makes me laugh. She is great fun, but she is Greek like us, and her eyes are like a cat's.'

'Have they any children, Aleko?'

'Two little girls who were born together.'

'You mean twins?'

'*Ne*. Papa says they are like peas out of a pod. That is funny, eh?'

'Yes.' Iris thought of the quiet, beautiful Fenella who had no children and she wondered how it affected her marriage to a Greek who was head of a vast organisation. If he had no son, then it looked as if in the future the small boy confronting her would be carrying a heavy load on his young shoulders.

'Can we go to the hotel now?' he pleaded.

'All right.' Iris stood up and smoothed her straight neat skirt. She felt inwardly nervous of entering the place, but inevitably she had to do so; she also had to brace her spine for her second meeting with Zonar Mavrakis. She couldn't forget those eyes of his and the way they had seemed to penetrate through the material of her convent uniform, a most disturbing feeling for a girl whose only knowledge of men came from the Jesuit priests who visited St Clare's.

She and Aleko left the villa in the afternoon sunlight, already slightly pink-tinged across the wide bay where the houses and buildings were terraced up the steep hillsides. She took a deep breath of the sea air and gazed in wonder at the scaly-trunked palms that grew out of the red soil of Tormont.

This part of the coast was called the Devon Riviera, and it was certainly very attractive and not in the least cold because it was sheltered by the high hills all around the bay. Limestone headlands contrasting with the red sandstone to create a perfect frame for the blue sea and the tropic trees.

A shock of excitement went through Iris as she and the boy rounded a bend in the road and found themselves upon a gradient leading down to the large courtyard of the Monarch Hotel. There were the swing doors, the long lower frontage of windows reaching almost to the ground, and rising above the massive white walls where the rooms had ironwork balconies. Some of the occupants sat upon their balconies beneath the shade of canopies, at ease in the sun.

Aleko ran down the gradient and Iris followed cautiously. The boy raced across to the doorman. 'I've come to see Papa,' he said eagerly. 'Where can I find him?'

The doorman raised an eyebrow and glanced at Iris as she crossed the forecourt towards the swing doors. 'This is Mr Mavrakis' little boy,' she explained, and tried desperately not to look as nervous as she felt. 'We've just come down from London and Aleko wants to say hullo to his father.'

The doorman swept a guarded look over Iris in her plain skirt and white blouse. She almost had to smile in case the man was wondering if she was the boy's mother. Holy heaven, what an idea!

'I am Aleko's governess,' she exclaimed.

'I see.' He conducted them into the hotel lobby, an enormous rotunda set around with showcases of jewellery, *objets d'art*, and cashmere jackets. There were marble columns, chandeliers overhead, and a couple of porters behind a desk at the back of which hung hundreds of keys on little hooks.

'Papa!' The boy darted across the rotunda and Iris watched as he was swept up into the arms of Zonar Mavrakis.

CHAPTER THREE

THE tall Greek looked as if he'd been busily at work most of the day; his tie was pulled loose from his shirt and his black hair was mussed as if he'd been dragging his hands through it. With great affection he kissed his son, who clung to the strong shoulders and nuzzled his face against the man. Iris felt the scene imprinting itself upon her mind, and the next instant her pulse gave a jolt as the compelling dark eyes fixed upon her.

He didn't smile but just looked at her, taking in deliberately the helmet of ashen hair above the slender contours of her face. Then his gaze slid downwards over her figure and Iris realised that now she was out of her uniform she looked more her age and less of a convent girl he had hired to take care of his son for the summer.

'Good afternoon, Miss Ardath.' He spoke English with a slightly grating accent. His voice matched his looks, for here in the vaulted foyer of the hotel he seemed even darker than Iris remembered ... hair, eyes and powerful jaw shaded by his sideburns and his imminent need of a shave.

'Good afternoon, sir.' Iris's voice held quiet cool tones learned from the nuns. She had a look of sedate composure as she bore his scrutiny, but it was hiding an uneasy nervousness inside her.

'I trust you had an interesting drive down from London?' Something came into his eyes, a look of amusement, or mockery.

'We very much enjoyed the drive, sir.' Iris felt herself going tense; here in these stylish surroundings she felt sure she looked oddly out of place, with her hair cut monklike, with her skirt too long and her shoes too flat. But Zonar Mavrakis knew her background and she decided it was rather cruel of him to find her ... comic.

'We will go to my office, come!' Still holding Aleko in his arms, he swung round. Over his shoulder he asked one of the porters to have coffee and biscuits sent in to him. He strode past the big reception desk, where one of the young women paused in her book-keeping and followed him with her eyes. Iris followed him through a door just beyond the desk and she felt the tremor in her hand as she closed it behind her and became part of the intimacy of a father with his son.

'Well, Aleko, what do you think of your governess?'

The boy leaned forward and whispered something in his father's ear. Iris felt her hands clenching together behind her and she wanted to protest that she wasn't here to provoke amusement, and Zonar Mavrakis should tell his son that it was impolite to whisper about people in front of them.

Then he said, amazingly: 'Now, Aleko, you will say aloud in front of Miss Ardath what you have just confided into my ear.'

Aleko cast her an impudent look. 'I have told Papa that you are to be a holy nun and so he had better not expect you to fall in love with him.'

'Really!' She flushed and felt as if she didn't know where to put her face.

'It's all right, Miss Ardath.' The Greek swung his son to the floor. 'Children have a disconcerting habit of revealing the naked truths we adults prefer to cover up. I do assure you that you will be returned to your convent as pristine as you arrived here. To a child everything is either more ominous or more profound than it really is, and a boy without a mother is constantly on the alert to see if his father is about to provide him with one. But I do assure you that the Reverend Mother made it perfectly clear to me that you are to enter the Holy Order of St Clare's when you return there, so please don't look at me as if I mean to endanger your plans. I assure you, young woman, nothing was further from my mind.'

As he spoke those words his eyes flicked her from head to heel, dwelling on those shoes that looked so clumsy on her feet. To her relief there came a knock on the door and he looked away from her. 'Come!' he said, in that deep voice that used certain English words so gratingly.

A waitress entered carrying a tray on which stood a coffee pot, large coffee cups instead of small ones, and a plate of biscuits.

'Please to put the tray just there.' The Greek gestured at a table near the window; a long window which overlooked the forecourt. 'You will join me, Miss Ardath?'

'We've had our tea, sir——'

'Nonetheless I would like you to join me. Please to bring a chocolate ice-cream for my son,' he said to the waitress. 'Ah yes, Miss Ardath, I know he has been eating candies and cakes, but just this once allow me to indulge him.'

'He's your son, Mr Mavrakis.'

'Indeed! And because he is my son I remember when I was his age and had no conception what chocolate ice-cream tasted like. I'm a Greek, Miss Ardath, and my son is special to me.'

'I'm sure he is——' Iris bit her lip. 'He's yours to spoil, of course.'

'Spoil!'

Iris looked steadily at the dark, distinct face and saw the twin lights of anger glimmering at the centres of his eyes. 'He does seem to get a lot of his own way, doesn't he, sir?'

'You think so, eh?'

'It would certainly appear so to me.'

'You come from a convent, miss.'

'That doesn't mean I was whipped and fed on bread and water, but a little discipline never hurt anyone.'

'I haven't hired you to be a disciplinarian where my son is concerned. I want a companion for him who will also be instructive when he asks questions, but I don't require for him a stick in a skirt!'

'I'm not——'

'No?' His lip curled slightly, and he glanced over at the desk where Aleko was sitting in the winged leather chair and looking as if butter wouldn't melt in his mouth. 'Aleko, what do you think of this young woman? Do you like her, or has she been in any way sharp with you?'

Aleko stared at Iris, and then he shook his head and smiled. 'She's all right, Papa. She made me wash my hands and face, though.'

'She did that, eh?'

Aleko nodded and picked up a gold pen from the desk. 'Can I have this, Papa? I like it.'

'And you'd very soon lose it,' Iris just had to say. 'Gold pens aren't for little boys and I'm sure you have coloured pencils in your playroom at the villa and when we get back we'll play with those.'

Aleko pouted a little and then laid down the pen. Zonar Mavrakis stood there and Iris was intensely aware that he was judging her. If he wished to send her back to St Clare's then let him do so, but she felt she was right to be firm with the child. Aleko wouldn't respect her if he could have all his own way with her, but if that was the sort of governess his father wanted for him, then he had better be rid of her right this minute.

'I have a colouring book filled with express trains,' Aleko scrambled off the chair and came running to her. 'Can we colour those when we go home? Can we, Miss Iris?'

'Of course.' She smiled and their fingers entwined. 'I like trains as well, not that I've travelled on many, only when we've been taken on a day's excursion with the Sisters. They're exciting, aren't they?'

He nodded, and then his father moved abruptly to the window table. 'Miss Iris, will you pour my coffee for me—I, too, like to be indulged.'

'Yes, sir.' She disentangled her fingers from his son's and was aware as she approached his tall figure, framed by the long window, that he was a complex man she wasn't going to find all that easy to get along with. He liked his own way! Was accustomed to it, especially where women were concerned. She was, she realised, unlike any other woman he had known ... she was on the other side of a barrier he was forbidden to cross.

'Do you take cream and sugar, sir?'

'Cream makes it lukewarm,' he said. 'The coffee in that pot is Greek and I won't have its flavour spoiled by sugar.'

'Then you like it as it comes, sir.'

'As I like most things,' he rejoined. 'Life is a challenge out here in the big raw world—as you are going to find.'

Discipline kept Iris's hand steady as she poured his coffee, but when she handed him the cup she had to look at him ... his eyes weren't mocking her, they were challenging her, and she felt her heart give a thump. For a wild instant she almost asked to be sent back behind the sanctuary walls of St Clare's where she'd be safe from the masculine self-will and dominance of this man who knew the world and its ways all too well.

She took a deep breath, but before she could speak the waitress entered with Aleko's ice-cream. 'I'd have some of that,' Zonar Mavrakis drawled. 'You might find Greek coffee a trifle too strong for you.'

'I'm sure I would,' she said. 'Especially the way you drink it, sir.'

'Of course, you are welcome to cream—from the look of you I shouldn't think you weigh much. I expect they kept you busy at the convent?'

'Yes, sir. The devil will always find work for idle hands.'

'You look at me, Miss Ardath, as if you think me in league with him.'

'Not at all, sir——'

'You protest too quickly, miss.' He emptied his cup and held it out for a refill. Iris, instinctively obedient, took the cup and poured the strong dark coffee from the pot. When she handed him the cup she again had to steel her nerves in order to meet his sardonic eyes ... irrationally she thought of what Aleko had told her about the brother's wife Fenella, to whom he spoke in deep gentle tones. Did he love her and was that why he remained a widower?

'You have guarded eyes, Miss Ardath, as I suppose

they would be in a girl who grew up behind the guarded walls of a nunnery. What does it feel like to be out in the world without a chaperone?'

'Strange,' she admitted, 'but interesting. Tormont appears to be very picturesque.'

'So you think you will enjoy the place? Yes, it is picturesque and I believe that was why I suggested to my brothers that we buy the Monarch. It's something of a place, eh? It has been established on this coast since the turn of the century when it used to cater for visiting royalty. It still has something of a reputation and the parts of it which haven't been modernised are rather impressive. This afternoon I have been taking a good look at the staff quarters and I don't like them. They are grim, like a barracks. There are members of the staff who sleep in and they should be made a little more comfortable, and I'm not keen on the room where they take their meal breaks. I have been shaking things up.'

Abruptly he smiled and instantly Iris understood why women were attracted to him. His smile deepened the lines of his face and played about in his eyes, it showed her a man who liked to enjoy life with the same vigour with which he worked. His eyes met hers and she felt as if an electrical tingle travelled along her spine ... instinct told her that in years gone by he had travelled along a dark corridor of emotional pain, that sorrow had penetrated deep into his bones, in his marrow, feeding his memories probably for a long time. He had emerged from that tunnel a man of strength and cynicism, as if he no longer believed that real happiness could be found again.

Instead he worked and played hard and for all her lack of worldliness Iris saw it in his lean, strong-boned face weathered by the winds of chance. Into that face had been carved years of striving, tenacious determination and a certain ruthless quality that finally veneers the features of the self-made man.

Iris wasn't to know it, but had she seen Zonar Mavrakis standing shoulder to shoulder with his brother Lion she would have been startled by their likeness to each other. Lion, however, had found happiness with a woman and it had mellowed him to a certain extent, but Zonar had grown in some ways hard and distant, softening only for his son, for the occasional girl who intrigued him, and for a young memory whose remains lay under the hard stony soil of Greece.

To look into his eyes, Iris thought again, was like flying through the spaces of night. Although he was a man who might know many people, he would always keep something of himself in reserve, detached from close contact of the heart.

Where women were concerned, Iris realised, he took, gave costly gifts in return, but never gave himself.

'Such a profound look,' he drawled. 'Are you trying to look into my soul, little nun?'

A sense of confusion swept over Iris, for that was what she had been attempting to do.

'People,' she said, 'are bound to make me curious for a while. The atmosphere inside a convent is secluded.'

'Because of the chastity?' he murmured. 'Where instincts of the flesh are subdued? Does it frighten you, Miss Ardath, to find yourself in the company of a man who finds self-restraint something of a mystery?'

'To be chaste isn't to be a prude,' she murmured. 'I didn't come out into the world expecting men of the world to be like the Jesuits. I'm not a child, Mr Mavrakis.'

'But do you really know your own mind?' He scanned her face through narrowed eyes. 'Look at Aleko over there enjoying his ice-cream and getting chocolate all round his mouth. Endearing, is he not? He is something a nun can never have. Are you really going to deprive yourself in that way?'

'I shall be rewarded in other ways, sir.' Iris tilted her chin and braved the cynical look in his eyes. 'You wouldn't understand.'

'I'm not of the stuff that martyrs are made, eh?' He searched his pockets and withdrew a cigar case, taking from it a thin dark cigar which he thrust between his lips. He spun the wheel of his lighter and bent his dark head to the flame, the westering light through the window showing the vagrant gleam of silver in his hair. Zonar Mavrakis was thirty-five and he looked every year of it ... it quickened strange fears in Iris when she thought of how experienced he was in contrast to herself, a girl of eighteen who would never give herself to any man.

There at the back of his dark head was the sun on fire, and the command and power of the man was somehow a little frightening in that moment, as they stood eye to eye and the strong but not unpleasant smoke of his cigar drifted into her nostrils.

The aroma seemed to intensify his maleness and for the first time in her life Iris was actively aware of the differences between a man and a woman. In thought, word and deed they were on opposite sides. They were rocky cliff and soft deep water. They were the supple pelt of the tiger, and the gliding wing of the swallow.

As the room deepened into hazy red shadow Iris couldn't take her eyes from that dark towering figure. He was a pagan and she would be living in his house

... her fingers crept to the cross she wore on a chain about her neck.

'Aleko is quiet.' Abruptly he crossed the room, his stride a long one. Then Iris heard him laugh softly. 'My son has fallen asleep, tired out with motoring and replete with ice-cream. My car is out on the forecourt, Miss Ardath, so I will drive you both home.'

Home! It was a word Iris wasn't accustomed to. A convent wasn't a home in the truest sense of the word; it was a house of prayer and service, where the physical loves of people were excluded.

'Come!' Zonar Mavrakis lifted his son into his arms. 'Let us go home.'

Iris followed him from his office and quietly closed the door. Out on the forecourt the sea air had grown chilly and she shivered. The sun had died away and lights were agleam in the houses across the bay.

'Into the car quickly,' the Greek commanded her. She obeyed him and he settled Aleko beside her, so the sleepy young head was at rest against her.

'The sea looks dark.' The words came over a broad shoulder as they drove uphill. 'Do you swim, Miss Ardath?'

'Yes,' she replied. 'We were taught at the local swimming-pools, but I expect the sea on this coastline is more challenging.'

'Indeed, a little like the Greek sea at times. You probably don't ride, eh?'

'No.'

'You must learn.'

'Must I, sir?'

'*Ne*, you will take lessons with Aleko. You aren't afraid of horses, are you?'

'I don't think so, sir.'

'But a little afraid of men, eh?'

'No——'

'Little nuns shouldn't tell lies,' he reproved her. 'I'm perfectly aware that you are afraid of me. It's natural, for a girl who has lived among devout women. I'm neither saint nor monk and I have no intention of behaving like one for your sake. You know it, don't you?'

'Yes.'

'Just as well to make things clear then you won't expect me to watch my every word and action. I speak my mind, Miss Ardath, and I lose my temper. I like to drink Chevas Regal and I have friends to the villa with whom I play cards. I may also invite friends of the opposite sex. You are welcome to disapprove of my habits, but don't attempt to reform me, will you?'

'I wouldn't dare to try, sir.'

'You would have a hard task on your hands if you attempted it! I am dyed in the wool by now.'

'Firmly attached to your pelt,' she said quietly.

'Huh, what is that you say, miss?'

'A tiger can't change its stripes, sir.'

'Are you scared of tigers?' His laughter came to her, soft and somehow insinuating in the darkness. The car curved into the driveway of the villa and suddenly there was light filtering out from the windows. The sound of the car had been heard and the front door swept open. Iris felt the little boy stir sleepily against her, snuggling his face into her. She sat there as Zonar Mavrakis slid out from behind the wheel, and when he reached for his son, his eyes met and held hers.

'Are you?' he said again. 'Scared?'

'A Sister at the convent once took us to the zoo,' she said. 'The tigers there were behind bars and I—I thought it was a shame.'

'Ah,' he spoke the word softly, 'there's more to you than meets the eye, isn't there?'

'Is there, sir?'

'Don't look so innocent,' he mocked. 'You look as if you've been fed on lemon leaves and herbs, but as we say in Greece, a frugal diet feeds the mind. I warn you, miss, there may be evenings here at Tormont when I shall invite you into my den. Will you dare to enter?'

'If you give the order, sir, then I'll have no option but to obey.'

'Obedience is a cardinal rule at St Clare's, eh?'

'It's a part of self-discipline,' she replied, and as he leaned there in the doorway he seemed to fill the world, big and demanding, and curious about her because she had lived such an enclosed life ... shut away from men such as himself.

'Are you totally self-disciplined, Miss Ardath?' He lifted his son carefully into his arms.

'No one can say that,' she replied carefully. 'I—I'm not a mouse, if that's what you're assuming, Mr Mavrakis.'

'What makes you think I am making assumptions about you, Miss Ardath?' He quizzed her face as they mounted the steps to the foyer of the villa. They entered beneath the pendant lamps that cast a warm glow and the maid closed the door quietly behind them.

'I imagine that you have an enquiring mind about everything and everyone,' Iris said in reply to his question. Aleko stirred awake and blinked his lashes. His father glanced down at him and a smile softened the firm outlines of his mouth.

'It's off to bed with you, my son, you have had a long day. You can have your supper tray in bed.'

'Do I have to go to bed, Papa?' The boy yawned widely. 'Can't I have supper with you?'

'I have to go out, *kalo pedhi.*'

'Business?' Aleko studied his father's face and pouted slightly.

'Of course.' They went up the stairs and Iris followed. Business, she wondered, or a woman with long sleek hair, wearing a dress that showed her shoulders, and shoes whose high slim heels brought her level with the bold mouth that looked as if it brooked no refusal when he was feeling ardent. Iris felt the flow and ebb of heat in her cheeks ... the man provoked thoughts she seemed unable to control, and a troubled look came into her eyes. She paused upon the gallery as he strode into Aleko's bedroom, a hand gripping the balustrade as she gazed around her.

This wasn't her kind of world, yet here she was. The sound of the sea drifted in through a window along the gallery, splashing in over the rocks to slap against the cliffside. She felt trapped inside a strange dream ... leave us for three months, Reverend Mother had said, and find out a little about life before you commit yourself to us. Discover if the world beyond our walls has more to offer than we have. You should know the answer within that scale of time.

But would she? Iris stood reflective, slim and fine-boned in her modest clothing, untouched by the kind of emotions and experiences which had made inroads into the nature of the man who had imperatively entered the enclosed order of her life.

A perplexed and wondering sigh stole from her lips ... she felt torn between a desire to explore this unknown world, and a need to be secure again behind the high safe walls of the convent. She felt as a marine creature must feel when it was flung upon a strange beach and stranded there until the tide came in and returned it to its own habitat ... in the meantime, however, it had to face the hazards of the unknown and possibly the unscrupulous.

When Reverend Mother had said that the Mavrakis family was a respected one, she had been speaking of the Greek clan in general; of their reputations as successful men of business.

Iris thought of how big and vital, how alive and aware was the Greek who had just carried his son off to bed, so he'd be free to go and enjoy the night life of Tormont ... just as he no doubt enjoyed the more sophisticated pleasures of Athens, Paris and London.

Mother Superior couldn't have realised, Iris thought. She believed that all men were like the good priests who called at the convent ... Iris was in no doubt that Zonar Mavrakis was totally unlike them!

The next few days were spent by Iris and Aleko exploring the delights of this town that sprawled on the edge of the sea. Its beach meandered in and out of coves and rock groins, sometimes wide and then narrowing to a bare strip of stony sand. Some of the stones were so colourful and smooth that Aleko started a collection of them and, of course, it was Iris who had to lug them home to the villa.

She found the sunsets across the bay a breathtaking wonder each evening; it was as if something in the sea drew forth an abundance of energy and colour from the dying sun, and the colours lingered, filling the sky with a canvas she never grew weary of looking at.

The terrace of the villa looked out over the sea and it felt good to linger there after an active day spent with an energetic child; she hadn't known that children could be so tireless, unless it was that Aleko had inherited the restless energy of his Greek father, who drove off early in the morning to the hotel and often didn't return until she had put Aleko to bed. The boy never slept until his father appeared in his room; the attachment between them was a very deep one, and Iris always made herself scarce when Zonar Mavrakis arrived home.

Out there on the terrace as dusk deepened she would catch the sound of masculine laughter from inside the house. She knew instinctively that the boy related events of the day to his father, who in his worldliness was probably amused by the idea of a young woman sharing in the childish pleasures of beachcombing, paddling, cave exploring, and feeding stale bread from the hotel kitchen to the insatiable gulls and pigeons down on the harbour.

Perhaps the Greek had never found the time to wander into old churchyards to read the fascinating country names on the tombstones. To eat toasted teacakes in quaint little tea-rooms. To visit a place like the model village a bus ride out of Tormont, where perfect replicas of manor houses, a railway station, cricket club, church and inn were built among miniature hills and dales in the exact stone, slate and thatching used for lifesize dwellings.

They had gone to the model village that day and now Iris felt pleasantly tired as she sat in a cane lounger and watched the stars twinkling over the still waters of the bay. Some nights the sea was restless and tormented and she'd lie in bed listening to the sound of it, but this evening the stillness was like a benediction. She breathed the soft air wafting in from the water ... God had made a wonderful world, she reflected, if only everyone would realise it.

'So here you are.' A thread of cigar smoke drifted from the open doors leading out to the terrace and as the aroma tickled Iris's nostrils, and the timbre of the deep voice came out of the darkness, she lost her sense of relaxation and sat up straight in the lounger.

'Aleko enjoyed his day, Miss Ardath.' The end of the cigar glowed like a red eye as he drew upon it. 'He said you drove to the fairyland by bus—the limousine and my chauffeur are at your disposal, you know.'

'Aleko enjoyed the bus ride, *kyrie*.'

'I daresay, but it rained somewhat and the buses are infrequent until the summer trade really picks up. Why not enjoy a little comfort while it's available; long years of self-sacrifice lie ahead of you, do they not?'

'I—I don't regard it in that way, sir.'

'I am a man, miss, who finds it a little hard to understand how a young woman can face the prospect of a life which will be devoid of many comforts and pleasures. You obviously have a way with children. Have you no wish to have a child of your own?'

'I've never really thought about it, sir.' Iris had noticed that when obliged to converse with Zonar Mavrakis she instinctively spoke in a cool and distant voice. She didn't really know why she felt a certain dread of him ... she admired his industry and his devotion to Aleko, yet whenever he spoke to her, she felt her spine stiffening like a poker. Added to which it seemed a rather personal subject for him to touch upon, almost as if he meant to disconcert her.

'Even young women reared in the convent tradition must wonder a little about the subject.' There was a note of insinuation in his voice, and Iris grew even more rigid as he strolled on to the terrace and she felt his tallness looming up beside her. The compulsion to run indoors was overwhelming for a moment and only her sense of discipline kept her from bolting away from him.

'It must have been a topic of conversation, girls being girls the world over,' he drawled. 'Or were you too busy at your devotions?'

'I don't really know why you should be interested, sir.' Her voice trembled slightly, with a mixture of nerves and a thread of temper. 'I came here to look after Aleko, but when I leave to return to St Clare's I shall do so in the full awareness that my vows exclude a—a child of my own. Other things will fill my life.'

'You haven't begun to live.' He tossed ash from his cigar, almost scornfully. 'I suppose you have been there from a child?'

'From a baby,' she admitted.

'And still in many ways as innocent as a baby.' He lounged there with his back to the terrace wall, his face in shadow except for the glint of his eyes, and the glow of the cigar when he drew upon it. 'I understand from Aleko that the pair of you were enraptured by this model village; two kids in fairyland, eh?'

'Is it so wrong to be—innocent?' she murmured. 'Does everyone in the world have to be a hard-headed realist?'

'Meaning me, Miss Ardath?'

'Yes, sir. Perhaps you never stood still long enough to appreciate what W. H. Davies wrote.'

'You think I have no time to stand and stare, miss?'

'I wonder if you've noticed, sir, that the view across the bay is beautiful, and the sounds of the sea aren't always the same. I hope you don't mind that I'm teaching your son to take notice of such things? You chose me for his governess knowing my world was so different from your own.'

'Quite deliberately,' he agreed. In the gleam of the lamps in grilles attached to the wall his smile was just perceptible, a faint and cynical twist of the lip. 'I had come to the conclusion that the world was full of good-time women, but my brother Heraklion suggested that I apply for a governess at a place where worldliness would be an unknown quantity. So what better place to choose than a house of nuns, and how accommodating of your Reverend Mother to permit a member of her brood to join my menage?'

The tip of his cigar smouldered red in the dusk. 'What opinion have you formed of my household?'

'The villa is very attractive,' she replied in her politest tone of voice. 'I like Tormont and enjoy Aleko's company.'

'What of mine, Miss Ardath?'

Her hand clenched the ironwork along the top of the terrace wall. What did she reply? Did she tell the truth, that he intimidated her and yet made her feel a tingling curiosity because he represented all that she had never experienced and was never likely to? He was part of a cosmopolitan world peopled by other successful men and elegant, charismatic young women such as the one he had escorted around Paris.

Iris not only suspected that he found her own naïvety a source of amusement—how could she help but notice the quirk to his eyebrow when he looked her over from her laced-up shoes to her monk-like hair?—but instinct told her that he was comparing her to the kind of girls he liked himself but whose sophistication he didn't wish his son to absorb until he was a little older.

A lamp bloomed inside the villa and its outflowing glow lit the terrace and the tall figure of Zonar Mavrakis as he began to pace slowly back and forth, silent-footed, an almost panther-like menace about him in the half-light ... as if the night beyond the house called to him and awoke in him a restlessness to hunt his prey.

'Aleko never knew his mother,' he said abruptly. 'She was young herself and she died even as he was born—a godforsaken fool drove his car into mine and my wife was hurled half through the windscreen. She should have been wearing her safety-belt, but she was eight months pregnant and found the belt uncomfortable. I should have insisted! I curse myself that I didn't do so! By the gods, does a man ever forget? The shock and pain and terror sent her into immediate labour and I delivered Aleko there at the roadside—can you understand what I went through? No, how could you when your view of the world has been through the stained-glass windows of a cloistered convent! How could you be expected to know anything of my kind of world?'

'I—I'm not a complete child, *kyrie*.' Iris felt a thrust of compassion for him, mingling with the reserve that wouldn't permit her to demonstrate her pity in a physical way. His kind of women reached out with their arms and gave him their curvaceous bodies so he might for a while forget the torn body of the girl he had loved and lost. Iris could only look at him with her large iris-coloured eyes and remain where she was, apart from him and tense, hands clasping the iron that was cool and hard in the night air filled with the smell of the sea ... the sea that shifted back and forth upon the far-down sands and stones.

The silence stretched as his cigar smoke eddied across the terrace and mingled in her nostrils with the scent of the sea. Iris stood there and felt in all her nerves the stride he took that brought him close behind her, tall, powerful, still suffering from a wound that time had not healed nor pleasure soothed except for an hour in scented arms.

'My wife was about your age.' His voice was above her head and yet deep in his throat. 'I was a young man myself in those days—the child she was carrying had been made with eager passion and love, but you would know nothing of that, eh? It is for you a sin to give your lips, to bind your arms about a man and permit him to make you mad with joy. Tell me, little nun-to-be, are you not curious about that kind of heaven?'

'No,' she said, and then gave a gasp as he slid a hand along her waist and pressed his fingers into her side. She jerked away from his touch, but not before she had felt a quivering leap of the senses, a soft fire that lapped her skin and probed her nerve-ends.

'Don't do that!' She swung round and backed along the terrace wall, as if shrinking away from actual fire. Her eyes were enormous, wide with shock and fear of his maleness. His eyebrows quirked and with a dismissive gesture he flicked the end of his cigar over the wall.

'I was merely testing you,' he drawled. 'I still find it hard to believe that I have a little saint on my hardened hands.'

'I—I don't pretend to be a saint.' She flung up her chin and hated it that for a moment he had made her feel helpless and afraid of him ... or had she felt more afraid of herself? 'I'm dedicated to what I want, and if there are rules, then I wish to obey them.'

'How very prim and proper,' he mocked softly. His

eyes slid up and down her slim figure in the plain and sensible clothes. 'Don't you feel a very human and female urge to wear pretty things? Is that also a sin?'

'It's a matter of finances. Pretty things cost money——'

'I have plenty of money, Miss Ardath.'

'W-what do you mean?'

'Come, you keep assuring me you aren't obtuse. I wish to buy you some more becoming clothes An account can be opened for you at Debenham's——'

'Indeed not!'

'By the gods, any other girl would leap at such an offer!'

'I daresay, *kyrie*, but all I want from you is what I earn.'

'What if I tell you, miss, that I don't wish my son to be seen with a governess who looks as if her clothing came out of a rummage sale? Those shoes are appalling and they look uncomfortable and heavy. That skirt has obviously had the hem taken up, and the blouse hangs on you like a sack. I insist upon opening that account for you and as your employer I insist that you go to Debenham's tomorrow and pick out some nice things to wear, for day and evening.'

'I—I can't accept your offer, Mr Mavrakis. If you don't like the way I look then I suggest that you find someone else to take care of your son.' On her dignity, Iris went to move past him so she could enter the villa, but swiftly he reached out and gripped her wrist in his hard fingers. She tried to pull away and at once he pulled her with ease towards him ... instantly she stopped struggling and gave him a defiant look.

'Don't try and fight me, Miss Ardath.' His smile was faintly cruel as he gazed down at her, his eyes as dark and menacing as the sea lost in the darkness. 'I'm not only bigger than you, but I'm far more ruthless. If you won't go voluntarily to the shop to choose a wardrobe, then I shall take you, and the saleslady will either think you my daughter or my lady love.'

'You wouldn't dare take me,' Iris rejoined, her fingers fluttering helplessly for escape from his grip.

'Dare a Greek and he'll do almost anything.' The firm white teeth glimmered against his dark skin. 'Now I come to think of it, it might be just as well that I take you to the shop and do the choosing. I doubt if you have the foggiest notion what suits you, for no doubt your pure young mind is filled with images of yourself in saintly robe and coif——'

'And what do you intend to put me into?' she flashed. 'A bikini for day and black chiffon cut down to my navel for the evenings?'

'Ah, so the little nun has a sharp little tongue, has she?' A mocking smile moved in and out of his eyes, like moonlight on dark water. 'No, my child, black chiffon is not for you. White is for you, and the deep purple-blue that will reflect those big eyes. The bikini I don't like anyway. The matter is settled that I shall choose for you. I shall enjoy it—seeing your discomfiture as you are made to look more like a girl and less like an acolyte.'

'You won't make me do anything——' Again she sought to escape him and found herself struggling as ineffectually as a moth on a pin. 'I didn't come here for this—oh, damn you, let me go!'

'That is a very naughty word from such as you,' he chided. 'You will have to wash your mouth out with vinegar and water.'

'You're very clever, aren't you?' Her eyes blazed up

into his. 'I'm a joke to you, a diversion, someone you can get a rise out of. I—I dislike you intensely!'

'Many people have,' he drawled. 'It is one of the expectations when a Greek goes into business. He's naturally competitive and each successful venture collects for him a new enemy or two. If I must number you among my enemies, Miss Ardath, then so be it. So long as you give my son all your care and attention, then I shan't quibble if you give me—crumbs.'

Iris stared up at his strongly defined face, at the slanting dark brows above the ironical eyes, at the bold mouth edged by lines of cynicism. Her heart hammered and she felt herself go weak. Oh God, what was he doing to her that she couldn't run from him even as he released her hand and indicated that she was free to leave the terrace?

'Go,' he taunted. 'I'm not stopping you, am I?'

'You mean,' she swallowed as if to ease the pulse that hammered in her throat, 'back to the convent?'

'No, little idiot!' He spoke explosively. 'Go and have your dinner, and stop fearing I shall seduce you if you accept a few dresses from me. It's all part of the position —your uniform if you like. Go, go and drink a glass of wine to bring the colour back into your cheeks.'

When he laughed, not loudly but with soft mockery, Iris fled through the open french windows, beneath graceful wands of Chinese glass that hung where the lightest breeze could set them delicately chiming. She heard them mingling with his mocking laughter and she wanted to keep on running, out of the villa, away from Tormont and this man in whom love was sealed in the dust with a dead Greek girl.

On the gallery Iris came to a breathless halt and found herself staring into the glass of one of the long oval windows. It gave back her image as in a glass darkly, pale blonde hair clinging around a pale face, eyes large and incredulous.

It was a sin for her to think of the kind of love that Zonar Mavrakis gave to women since the loss of the girl who, with her dying breath, had given him his son.

Was it for the sake of Aleko that she stayed in this house? Iris pressed a hand to the little gold cross that hung in the pool of her neck ... she had to believe it was for the boy's sake. She didn't dare to face the possibility that it was the father who had captivated her, with his strange and ruthless charm.

CHAPTER FOUR

THE morning was balmy, with a blue sparkle to the sea beneath the terraced red hills. Already yachts were out in the bay and the shoreline rocks were mantled with curls of seaweed that glinted coppery-green in the sunlight. The rock pools gleamed, and birds skimmed through the crystal air and settled on the giant rocks deep in the water.

'In you get.' The passenger door of the Jaguar car was held open and Aleko scrambled in first, while Iris followed more sedately. She kept her gaze averted from the tall figure in impeccable grey suiting, and as she sank back against the soft leather of her seat she could feel a tremor in her legs. She tried to suppress her nervousness, to be in control of herself as she had learned to be at the convent.

This was ridiculous. Zonar Mavrakis was just another man, but when he glanced into the car and she was obliged to look at him out of politeness she knew he radiated a masculine force which made everything around him more vital and expectant.

Aleko had been told that they were going into town to buy her some new clothes, and with a grin he asked his father what they were going to do with her old ones.

'We shall make a bonfire of them—especially the shoes.' Zonar flicked his eyes up and down her tense figure there against the grey-blue leather of the sleek dark-blue car.

'You will do nothing of the sort, sir,' she protested. 'I shall need them when I return to St Clare's.'

'Really?' He raised a black eyebrow. 'You'll be taking your vows and covering yourself in black linen, won't you?'

Her eyelashes quivered as she bore his compelling gaze, and then to her chagrin she blushed until her earlobes stung. 'One of the other girls will need the clothes,' she said primly.

'Poor little charity girls,' he murmured, and then he closed the car door and swung into the driver's seat in front of Iris and the boy. She gazed at the barbered black hair and the broad shoulders to which the grey material was melded like a supple skin. She saw the movement of his back muscles as he started the car and drove it smoothly down the incline that would take them past the hotel and down to the harbour where the shops were situated along the Parade.

'Are you going to buy me a present, Papa?' Aleko demanded.

'If you behave yourself,' Zonar replied. 'Have you something special in mind?'

'I need a diving-suit for my Action Man,' said Aleko. 'What is it like to dive right down into the sea, Papa? Is it coloured down there?'

'The sea life and the fauna are coloured. It's a strange, timeless, cool world, and when you are a little older I shall teach you myself to dive. Have patience, little one, there is much for you to learn and enjoy as you grow up, but first you must reap the pleasures of childhood. You are more fortunate than Miss Iris was, or myself when a boy. Your uncles and I slept on sacking on the floor of a shack, our cupboard was a wooden box, and an old stove smoked in one corner and half choked us with the smell of burning charcoal which we collected from a railway siding. Hard times, Aleko *mou,* which perhaps made us hard.'

Aleko reached out when his father said that and his small hand touched the grey-clad shoulder. 'You feel hard, Papa.'

A brief laugh came from the man as he guided the Jaguar into parking space along the harbour wall. They climbed out and Iris stood breathing in the tangy air that wafted up from the waters of the harbour where birds were pecking in the shadows for stranded shrimp. There were a pair of swans lazing in the shadows of the wall, and rising above the town on terraces of rock were clusters of houses and a narrow-towered church that stirred and boomed the hour.

'It is like a picture postcard.' For an instant a large hand rested upon Iris's shoulder and light as the touch had been she felt it all the way down her spine, to the base, a tingling awareness of the man and the moment.

This I shan't forget, she thought, when I'm back at the convent and I take those vows that will separate me for all time from a man such as Zonar Mavrakis.

'Come!' He ushered the pair of them across the road, towards the big shop in whose windows stood lifelike models wearing the kind of clothes Iris had never dreamed of owning. She felt reluctant to enter the big shop, so instilled in her was the sense of self-denial, and as if sensing this her Greek employer took her by the elbow and urged her through the doors. He was in charge and it took him but a moment to establish that the fashionwear department was on the second floor. They entered the elevator and Iris cast a glance of apprehension and wonderment at the dark, determined face.

What kind of clothes had he in mind for her? Surely

he must realise that she wasn't the type who could be turned into a fashion plate!

Almost as soon as they entered the showroom a saleslady was at his elbow and Iris didn't know where to look when the woman asked in her bright, ready-to-sell voice if she could show *his wife* the new range of summer wear which had been delivered only a few days previously.

'Please do so,' he said, without bothering to correct the assumption that Iris was his wife. 'We wish to see a full range of day and evening wear, and the accessories, of course.'

'Of course, sir.' The woman clasped her hands and studied Iris, slightly raising an eyebrow as she took in the dowdy clothes that contrasted oddly with the suit Zonar was wearing. 'Lingerie, hose and shoes? Am I correct?'

'Absolutely.' He glanced around him, very tall and dark in the mirrored salon, with its glass-fronted cabinets of feminine array. 'Spare no expense. We are shopping for the best.'

'If madame will come to a cubicle I'll take her measurements.' Iris was measured again by those calculating eyes, then they slid downwards to her clenched left hand and saw that it was ringless. Iris could sense acutely what the woman was wondering, and then Aleko spoke:

'Can I come and see you measured?' he asked.

'No, you can't, young man.' It was his father who replied, a rather droll note in his voice. 'You will behave yourself, and afterwards you can have ice-cream.'

'All right.' Aleko began to wander around the salon, pausing to study some very high-heeled shoes on a stand. 'Are you going to buy these for Iris?' he asked, casting a cheeky grin over his shoulder. 'I bet she'd fall over in them.'

'That range of shoes are from Italy, sir,' the saleslady said at once, and an insinuating note had crept into her voice. 'They are very fashionable and flattering to the foot and leg. Would—madame care to try on a pair?'

'No, I shouldn't,' Iris said decisively. 'Those shoes are not my style.'

'No,' Zonar agreed. 'The heels are ridiculously high and they throw a woman forward and place the spine out of line. If a girl has a good straight spine, then it seems a pity to ruin it by trying to walk on stilts. Let us see some dresses and then we'll look at shoes with slim straps and a more moderate heel.'

'As you wish, sir.' The woman gave him a flattering smile, then asked Iris to come with her to a cubicle. Once inside the woman's smile slid from her face and again she looked Iris up and down. Iris decided that it was time to correct the assumption that she was either wife or mistress to the wealthy Greek.

'Mr Mavrakis is my employer,' she explained. 'I look after his son and he feels it's in keeping with his position for his son's governess to look a little smarter. I really need only a few things——'

'Is he paying for them, madame?'

'Yes——'

'Then let me suggest that you permit him to buy for you whatever takes his fancy.' The woman flicked open the buttons of Iris's blouse, feeling with her fingers the inferior quality of the material. 'We have some very nice dresses and suits in at the moment, and the new line in silk shirts is out of this world. Shantung silk imported from the Far East, expensive but worth every penny. From the look of your—employer I'd say that he can well afford the best.'

Iris could feel herself trembling slightly. She wasn't used to undressing in front of someone else, least of all a woman to whom the term governess seemed to signify something a lot more intimate. A sense of torment swept over Iris. It was cruel of Zonar Mavrakis to put her through this when he knew that in a matter of weeks she was going to put out of her life all the things that pandered to the flesh. He was forcing her to feel the sensuality of silk against her bare skin, the fragrance of scent, and sheer hose clinging to her legs.

He wasn't being generous to his son's governess ... he was playing a subtle game with her innocent, untried feelings, and Iris knew it even as she submitted to having her bosom, waist and hips measured.

'Madame is very slim,' the saleslady complimented her. 'The new styles will suit your figure, though a longer hairstyle is more fashionable at the present time. You could for the evenings buy one of the long sleek wigs—shall I suggest that to the gentleman?'

'No!' Iris's eyes widened with indignation. 'I'm accepting a few dresses from him because he insisted, but I'm nothing at all to do with his—his social life.'

'As madame says. I'll go and consult him about what he'd like you to try on.'

'Yes.' Iris said it with quiet resignation. 'He'll insist on doing the choosing, he's that sort of man.'

And for the next hour or so Iris was obliged to try on a variety of garments, each time emerging from the cubicle so her employer could inspect her from every angle, to either nod his satisfaction, or shake his head. A coat and skirt in peach wool. A blue linen with a navy silk tie. A doeskin jacket and skirt in honey-brown.

A blazer striped in sea-blue and cedar, with a slim white skirt. Sailcloth shorts, and Iris begging him with her eyes to make this the final selection.

But Zonar Mavrakis then wished to inspect her in evening dresses ... a polka-dot dress of apricot and white crêpe-de-chine, figured muslin in deep grape-blue, white pleated silk with georgette sleeves, the long skirt full and supple; a velvet dress, almost medieval in design, beneath which her breasts had a delicate outline.

'I like this one very much.' Zonar walked around her in the dress and she felt as if his eyes were touching her as they slowly travelled over her. 'Yes, this particular gown suits her skin and hair and blends with her personality.'

'I did suggest to madame,' said the salesday, 'that she try one of the sleek wigs that go so well with evening wear.'

'That won't be necessary.' He frowned at the woman. 'I'm not keen on that kind of falsity, least of all in connection with a girl of Miss Ardath's type. I should now like her to try on some shoes.'

Iris's feet were measured and then slipped in and out of the smartest footwear the shop had to offer. Cool lacework sandals, navy-blue and white classics, evening suede with diamanté ankle straps, cuban-heeled walkers with a T-bar. Then hosiery and lingerie were selected for her, and several handbags, and by this time Iris was too stunned by her sudden affluence to protest when ordered to wear one of her new dresses and a pair of the new shoes.

'What about my own clothes?' she asked, when she emerged in a print dress that fitted her with such perfect ease, her feet feeling as light as air in the soft leather that now moulded them. She held her bundle of belongings and gazed at her employer with a mixture of shyness and defiance. He took the bundle from her and handed it to the saleslady.

'If you would be so good as to dispose of this,' he said. *'Efharisto.'*

'Y-you can't throw them away,' Iris gasped, making an attempt to snatch back the convent clothing in which she felt she belonged. 'It would be wasteful——'

'Go ahead and dispose of them,' he told the saleslady. 'The new garments are to be sent to this address along with the account.' He handed her a card, wished her good day, then ushered Aleko and the protesting Iris into the lift.

'Do stop going on about those old rags,' he ordered, as the lift dropped to the ground floor. 'You might instead have the grace to thank me for all the nice things I've bought you.'

'T-thank you,' she mumbled. 'You've bought far more things than I shall need——'

'Nonsense. You must stop thinking of yourself as a charity child fit only to wear the discarded garments of someone else. Come, you must like the look of yourself after so many years of looking dowdy—Aleko, what do you think of Miss Iris's new look?'

The boy smiled at her. 'You look pretty,' he told her. 'Will the nuns mind you wearing a dress like that?'

Iris didn't know what to think, she only knew that trying to oppose the will of Zonar Mavrakis was like wrestling with the devil. When he set out to have his way he somehow had it, and here she was, dressed by him from neck to toe and feeling guilty about it.

'I—I shall only be able to wear these things while I'm at Tormont,' she explained to Aleko. 'That's why feel your father has been too extravagant.'

'By the gods,' Zonar exclaimed, 'your modesty is too ood to believe in! Dare you eat a peach Melba, or will hat require a penance?'

'You just wouldn't understand——' Her eyes met his, attling bravely with the devilish glint deep down in heir darkness. 'I appreciate your generosity, sir, but I nustn't put a high premium on worldly goods. You nustn't try to make me do that.'

'Don't tempt me,' he growled. 'All right, Aleko, you vill get your toy and then the two of you can eat ice-ream while I call in at the bank to sign some papers. I hink we'll have lunch at the hotel, eh?'

'Yes,' Aleko said gleefully. 'And roast beef off the rolley, with baked potatoes and pudding!'

'So speaks my Greek son,' Zonar drawled. 'Here is the noney, Miss Ardath, to purchase the toy and the re-reshments. You will meet me at the car in about one our.'

He strode off among the people thronging the arade, turning the corner that took him uphill to the ank. The toyshop was in the other direction and once nside that beguiling place it took Aleko some time to ull over the contents, taking as much care to select a uit for his Action Man as his father had taken to select arments for Iris.

She felt strangely unlike herself in the well-fitting ress and every now and again her hand would caress ne material. She had been taught that vanity was a n, but it did feel nice to be wearing shoes that didn't eigh like lead on her feet.

'I've decided.' Aleko was tugging at her hand. 'The e-breaker outfit.'

'Are you sure?' She quizzed the price tag and took

out the money from her new bag. She paid for the outfit and they made their way to the ice-cream parlour where Aleko had a banana split while Iris enjoyed a coffee cream.

The gulls winged in the sunlight over the harbour and in a ray of brightness her gaze dwelt on the child beside her, busily spooning his bananas and cream, a raven gleam to his hair. As if feeling her gaze he glanced up at her and she felt a tiny stab under her ribs.

'Is it nice?' she asked.

He nodded dreamily. 'Delicious. Is yours nice?'

'It melts on the tongue,' she smiled.

'Do you get ice-cream at the convent?' he asked.

'Sometimes Sister Mary makes it as a special treat. She's in charge of the kitchen.'

'Will you be called Sister Iris?'

'Very likely, unless Reverend Mother decides on a religious name for me.'

Aleko glanced down, his fine dark brows coming together in a frown. 'I wish you could always stay with Papa and me. Do you really have to go back to that place? Wouldn't you sooner be with us?'

'People have to do their duty, Aleko, and it's mine to go back to St Clare's when the time comes so I can join the Order and start my vocation. In the meantime we'll enjoy ourselves, won't we?'

He nodded and captured a cherry on his spoon. 'Would you like this?' he offered.

She accepted the cherry, knowing he wanted her to have it, and felt an impulse to hug him to her. Such impulses had to be suppressed, for the child's sake and her own. Eventually they must part to go their separate ways ... why, she wondered, didn't Zonar Mavrakis take a second wife so the boy could have the mother he needed? Even if he couldn't love a woman as he had loved Aleko's mother, he could be generous, and he was obviously a man whose vigour needed its outlets.

'All finished?'

Aleko nodded and she wiped his mouth with a Kleenex and they wandered out into the sunshine. There was a bakery a few doors along and Aleko persuaded her to buy some bread rolls so they could feed the birds that were so rampant upon the cliffs overhanging the town. They crossed the road to the harbour and the moment they scattered the bread the gulls were swooping down and grabbing the morsels, making loud mewing noises, as pretty as they were greedy.

Iris was unaware that her employer was watching until she and Aleko reached the car, where he lounged against the sleek hood, smoking a cheroot. Aleko ran to him, full of chatter about what they had been doing, and he smiled so directly into Iris's eyes that she felt a confusion sweep over her as she drew near to his dark, powerful figure. She stood looking at him, feeling as if she had lost the power of speech and movement; only her thoughts were busy:

'He's tremendous! I shall put myself in danger of liking him in the wrong sort of way if I stay in his house! Reverend Mother will make allowances if I leave now, but if I stay ... oh, if I stay, what will happen to me?'

'Are you planning to walk back?' He was holding open the car door and Iris had to move closer to him in order to enter the Jaguar. As she slid inside the skirt of her dress rode up slightly and she felt his gaze upon her legs as she drew them sedately together and pulled the hem of her dress down over her knees. She knew without looking that he smiled at her involuntary action, then he had swung in behind the wheel and the car was moving with powerful ease and silence away from the harbour.

'I'm ravenous,' Aleko announced. 'I can't wait for my lunch!'

'The sea air has given you an appetite.' Iris smoothed his hair and took a look at his hands. 'They'll have to be washed before you sit down to your lunch, young man.'

'I stroked a seagull, Papa. She let me, didn't she, Iris? She was so tame I bet I could have made a pet of her.'

'A creature so free and wild can never be truly tamed, Aleko *mou*,' his father said. 'She came to you for the bread and when it was all gone she spread her wings and flew away. Not all creatures will allow you to cage them and if you try, they might bite off your hand or mope in a corner until you are forced to release them. Think how miserable you would feel if that happened.'

Aleko nodded. 'All the same, Papa, she felt all warm and quivery, and her eyes were so bright. I bet I could have picked her up.'

'She'd have drawn blood,' Zonar drawled as he pulled into the driveway of the Monarch Hotel. 'Now let us go and have some of that beef and potatoes you fancy so much.'

The dining-room was large and overlooked the sea, and as Zonar's private table was beside the window they had a good view across the bay. Iris accepted a menu and was conscious that she was being studied by the hotel guests at nearby tables. They knew she was with the proprietor of the Monarch and like the woman in the dress shop they were more likely to regard her as the man's companion rather than the boy's.

It was the look of him, Iris thought helplessly; so very male and commanding that a girl in his company was bound to look as if she belonged to him.

'What do you fancy?' He looked directly across at her and in the sea-light she saw glints of amusement in his eyes. He knew as well as she what people were thinking, and as if to add fuel to the fire he leaned forward and indicated one of the selections. 'I can vouch for the fresh salmon, or do you fancy the buttered sole or the *coq au vin*, which is breast of bird cooked in wine and herbs?'

'I—I rather fancy a cheese omelette——'

'Come, you are hungrier than that after such a busy morning. Have you ever tasted salmon which hasn't come out of a can?'

'Even the canned variety, *kyrie*, was beyond the resources of St Clare's. You mustn't encourage me to get a taste for rich living.'

'More penance to pay if I insist that you try the salmon along with me?' Suddenly his eyes were unamused and there was a slight, rather angry flare to his nostrils. 'I'll be damned if you'll practise self-denial while you live under my roof. Is it to be salmon, beef off the baron, or bird in wine? Choose instantly!'

'You can be quite the bully, can't you?'

'Yes, when I am up against female obstinacy. First the dresses and the torment of wondering what category of sin that fell into, and now a cutlet of salmon! I merely treat you as I treat my son, like the father you never knew.'

Iris gazed at him speechlessly.

'I could be.' His smile was wicked. 'Boys grow up quickly on the streets of Sparta, and so do the girls. You have been too sheltered from life, as if pressed between the pages of a religious rule-book, so that even the sun stroking your skin must feel as if it's taking a liberty.'

The sun through the windows was warm on her bare arms and the atmosphere in this long room was pleasant, with its tables well spaced on a resilient carpet and set with snowy linen, shining cutlery and gleaming glassware. It was all so much in contrast to the spartan life she had known for such a long time; the food smelled rich and the diners had the same look of confidence and ease as her employer. They chatted effortlessly to each other; broke bread and drank wine with such a relaxed air, as if unaware that the money they spent on a single meal might provide a poor family with food for several days.

'Lotus-eaters,' she murmured.

'And I daresay that like my brothers and myself they have worked for it.' Zonar gave her a sudden hard look. 'Don't be such a sanctimonious little prig or I might decide that you aren't good company for Aleko and pack you off back to your walled-up world.'

'Perhaps that would be best——' She looked at him uncertainly.

'No,' Aleko suddenly grabbed her by the wrist, 'I don't want you to go back there! You've only been here a while and you're supposed to stay all the summer. You promised, Iris! I like you even if Papa doesn't think you're as nice as *his* other girl-friends. They smell of scent and they're always looking at themselves and combing their hair or putting red stuff on their lips. They get on my nerves—though I suppose the one in Paris wasn't so bad.'

'There's no need for impudence,' Zonar reproved his son.

'Well, you're not to send Iris away,' Aleko rejoined.

'Tomorrow we're going to see the caves at Shellstone and we're going there on the bus. We've made lots of plans, Papa. She's very good company, better than being with Achille, who says I talk too much, especially when he's trying to pick out his winners.'

Zonar regarded his son with a quizzical look on his face. 'One way or another, Aleko *mou*, you are going to pick up the habits of a sinner or a saint, aren't you? It had better be the saint, eh?'

Iris bit her lip at the mockery threading his deep voice, then he beckoned the waiter and said they were ready to order their meal.

'Have you decided what you want?' he asked her.

'The roast beef,' she said, with a hint of defiance.

'And for a starter?' His lips twitched.

'Melon, please.'

'The young people will have melon,' he said deliberately, 'then the roast beef and usual trimmings. I shall start with the liver *pâté* and proceed with the salmon and a salad.' Having ordered, Zonar glanced around the dining-room and nodded in a satisfied way. 'We seem quite busy today, Ferdi. Things look as if they are going smoothly.'

'They are, Mr Mavrakis. The new kitchen arrangements are working well.'

'Good. If there is confusion in the kitchen, then it causes delays and customers become irritated. I'm pleased.'

The waiter smiled quickly, then went off to fetch their first course, while another appeared almost at once, the foiled neck of a bottle jutting from a silver bucket. Zonar withdrew the bottle and examined the label, then he glanced across at Iris.

'You are about to be introduced to Dom Perignon.'

he informed her. 'If there's a wine of the gods, then you are about to taste it.'

Iris watched as the champagne was poured into glasses shaped like slim tulips. She could feel the rather mad beating of her heart as the sun found its way into the wine; it sparkled invitingly and she tried not to think of St Clare's, where the nuns and their pupils would now be sitting in the refectory, drinking water with the meal.

'Yes, just a little for the boy,' Zonar told the sommelier. 'It's such excellent wine that it won't do him any harm.'

Aleko grinned happily at Iris, and she just had to smile back at him. It wasn't easy, she realised, for Zonar Mavrakis not to spoil the boy. Love did appear to be that kind of emotion; an urge to be generous beyond measure to the person inside your heart.

Zonar raised his glass, first to his son, and then to Iris. '*Panta khara*, as we say in Greece. Be always happy, if that is possible.'

As Iris took a sip of the delicious wine she couldn't resist stealing a look at Zonar. His dark brows brooded above his eyes, looking out at the sunlit sea is if his thoughts had taken wing to Greece and the fleeting happiness he had known there. It hadn't lasted for him, and Iris saw his fingers clench around the stem of his glass and the gold rings held her gaze, one of them drawn from the hand of a dead girl and replaced on his hand, perhaps with a kiss.

'The climate here at Tormont is certainly inviting,' he remarked. 'It's a pictorial coastline and rampant with history. Yes, it was a good place to buy an hotel. What do you think of the Monarch, Miss Ardath?'

'Rather breathtaking,' she admitted. 'It must have

been established many years ago, but I can see that parts of it have been modernised.'

'Discreetly so,' he agreed. 'In the last few years it has not paid its way, but that will alter now it's part of the Mavrakis Corporation. I have noticed a little local opposition to the fact that I am a foreigner, but I have a tough skin, and a tougher determination to make this venture a successful one. In a few weeks my brother Lion and his wife will be coming to stay here—you will like her!'

'If you don't suddenly decide that hiring me was a mistake.' Iris felt her pulses give a jolt at the thought of meeting his intimidating older brother, head of the corporation, who had initiated their rise from rags to riches.

'I wonder about that,' he said drily. 'You sip your Dom Perignon as if it were fruit-salts stinging your nose. Don't you like it, you strange girl?'

'Yes, but I have so much to get used to. You don't seem to realise——'

'There you mistake me.' He smiled briefly. 'I do realise, or I am beginning to. You are like a small fish which has been taken from its bowl and plunged into a big pool. You are confused, and I must make the necessary allowances when you don't snatch at the tit-bits but regard them with a suspicious wonderment.'

When he looked at her like that, almost with gentleness, Iris felt the wine glass become unsteady in her hand. She put it down in case she upset the wine and exasperated him. She was an oddity he was trying to come to terms with, accustomed as he was to girls who drank his champagne and accepted his presents with insouciance. The intent look he was giving her, there in the play of sunlight, was proof enough that he was as perplexed by her as he was amused.

She and Aleko had scooped melon, the fruit chopped up into a delicious mixture with pineapple. Zonar spread *pâté* on wedges of crisp toast and talked of the difference in the colouring of his homeland and that of Devon. It had surpised him to find the fields of England so green. 'I wonder if the British people realise how restful it is for someone to come from a hot land into the cool green depths of your countryside? It has an effect that is very soothing to the spirit, but I have to say that your city hotels are in the main a disaster. For hotel comfort I prefer Athens.'

'Athens must be a very interesting city.' Iris looked across into the bold Greek face into which the pagan sun of his land had burned itself. She felt that her own skin must look egg-white by comparison ... two people who were as opposite as ice and fire.

'It teems with history, with life, with traffic, much as London does. There is a section of the city known as the Plaka which has a great deal of fascination. It is very old and secretive, very Byzantine, its houses and shops crowding each side of narrow stone stairways. There you will hear the music of Greek drums and the *bouzouki,* and the constant click of beads running through the fingers of the men and women. There you will find strange goods on display and you will feel as if you have stepped back in time. It's a place where a woman shouldn't walk alone.'

He had walked there with a woman, Iris thought, perhaps with his arm around her as they paused to look at the stalls in the shadow of the ancient walls, his lean fingers reaching for a Byzantine trinket for the girl to wear against the sun-tinted skin of her neck.

'You have large eyes, Miss Ardath, but they aren't

easy to read. You would enjoy the Plaka, I think.'

'It sounds very interesting,' she agreed.

'But you don't think you will ever get there, eh?'

'It seems doubtful. I shall have my work and we only receive a nominal wage. Sometimes outings to Rome are arranged and I may be lucky enough to go there one day.'

'In your middle years?' His lip gave a cynical twist. 'When youth and eagerness have been worked out of you?'

'You wouldn't understand——'

'Why, because I'm a sort of pagan in your eyes; a man who strives for success and enjoys the rewards?' His eyes narrowed as he looked across at her. 'What makes you think you're so saintly? Women aren't called the work of the devil for nothing!'

Iris caught her breath, not so much at what he said but at the way he looked ... he glowered from beneath his black brows, as if he wanted to reach out and shake her until her teeth rattled.

'I feel sure you know all about women.' She had said it before she could restrain herself, and then saw his lip curl into a slightly derisive smile.

'A lot more than you know about men,' he agreed.

At which juncture a chef arrived with a smoking side of beef on a trolley, steam drifting from the gravy and vegetables in their dishes. A shining knife sliced through the meat as Aleko watched eagerly. He was so much like his father, Iris thought; he reached out to grab at life and what it offered.

'It looks scrumptious,' he breathed.

'It is, young man.' The chef smiled down at him. 'Do you think you can manage three baked potatoes?'

'Yes, please, and lots of gravy. I like gravy.'

'I can see you do.' The chef glanced at Zonar Mavrakis. 'This is the first time I've met your son and daughter, sir.'

Iris didn't know where to look, while Aleko broke into a gleeful laugh at his father's expense. To Iris's relief her employer didn't take the remark too seriously; in a dry tone of voice he explained that she was Aleko's governess.

'I must apologise——' The chef went as red as the beef he was carving.

'There is no need.' Zonar's lip twitched. 'I am, after all, old enough to be her father—Aleko, if you spread any more mustard on that meat it will be uneatable. Replace the pot at once.'

'I like mustard, Papa——'

'There are things we all like, but you can have too much of a good thing. Is your tongue stinging?'

Aleko nodded and Zonar requested that the chef add a little more gravy to the boy's dinner in order to wash the mustard off his beef. 'As you can see,' he drawled, 'a son is enough for a busy Greek to handle, especially if he has no wife.'

The chef nodded and looked relieved that he hadn't offended the man who was his employer as well. Zonar's choice of salmon was served and they proceeded with lunch, Aleko shooting wicked little glances back and forth at Iris and his father.

'Yes, you find it highly amusing, don't you?'

'Can't I pretend that Iris is my sister, Papa?'

'No, you can't.' Celery crunched between the hard white teeth. 'She is your governess and you will treat her with due respect.'

'Why haven't I got a sister?' Aleko demanded, stuffing baked potato and brussel sprout into his mouth.

'Because that is the way of it—you have gravy running down your chin, wipe it off at once.'

Aleko scrubbed at his face with his napkin, but kept his large dark eyes pinned upon his father's face. 'I could have a sister if you got married again, Papa.'

'You think so, eh?' Zonar replenished the wine glasses and Iris felt the coolly amused flick of his eyes across her face. 'Why all of a sudden this interest in an enlargement of our family? I thought you and I were sufficiently content with each other.'

'It would be someone to play with, when you're busy,' Aleko pointed out. 'I don't see why you can't make Iris my sister, then she wouldn't ever need to go back to that place behind the walls. It looks very grim, and I don't think they have a great deal to eat.'

'Well, your Iris is making up for it at the moment, is she not? The beef is to your liking, Miss Ardath?'

'It's delicious, thank you.' She wished Aleko wouldn't keep on about his father adopting her; she sensed that it amused her employer in a subtle, rather edgy way. 'It's kind of you to bring me to the hotel for lunch.'

'Didn't you think I could be kind?'

'Yes, but a governess doesn't expect this kind of treatment.'

'What does she expect?' His glance held hers, taunting her a little. 'Do you mean I shouldn't place you in the position of being mistaken for my daughter?'

She hesitated a moment, then nodded. 'I'm sure you felt embarrassed——'

'Don't be sure of my feelings, Miss Ardath. It takes a lot more than that to make me hot under the collar. Perhaps you were embarrassed by the misconception?'

'I'm sure I don't look all that young.'

'Meaning, then, that I don't look so very old?'

'I'd hardly apply that word to you, sir.' She ducked her head and hurried on with her lunch. Now she wanted it to end so she and Aleko could return to the villa, leaving Zonar behind his desk at the hotel. But it wasn't to be that way; he fancied to have coffee in the sun-lounge and there it was served at a table beside the long range of picture windows, below which the surface of the sea was fractured by the down-beating sun.

'It really has been quite a day.' Zonar stretched his long frame in an armchair, the leaf wrapping of a cigar crackling in his fingers. A smile came and went about his lips as he clipped the cigar and applied a match to it from a folder with a picture of the Monarch on the front. He slowly shook out the flame and emitted the fragrance of the cigar, watching the smoke drift above her head.

'You take life quite seriously, don't you, Miss Ardath?'

She sipped her coffee, sitting upright in her own armchair. Aleko had curled drowsily into one of the window-seats and was ready to take a nap after his big lunch. Only a few other people sat about in the lounge and the atmosphere was quiet ... almost intimate.

'I'm not a frivolous person,' she replied.

'No, you have a quaint air of composure which is not unwelcome to a harrassed man of business. Having grown up in a convent you have never been allowed to be boisterous, eh?'

'I was never boisterous by nature, sir.'

He watched her from under his eyelids, smoke slightly blue-tinged playing over his head. 'Yet it's natural in a girl to want a little fun from life. You can't turn yourself into a mature woman by cutting out your best years—like cutting roses in the bud, before they've had a chance to open in the sun.'

'Those years will be put to good use——'

'By the gods, what does that mean?'

'I should think the meaning is perfectly clear, sir.'

'You really are aware of all you are throwing away in order to be of use, as you call it? There are many other ways of being useful without shutting the door on a normal life—there can't be all piety in your youthful soul, there must be some romance?'

'Romance is another word for fairytale——'

'And who told you that?' he demanded.

'My own common sense, sir.'

'To the devil with common sense at your age,' he said crisply. 'Don't you want to dance and flirt and be kissed in the moonlight? Have you been taught that the longings of the body are sinful and must be repressed until they die of starvation and sanctify you?'

'Whatever my feelings, Mr Mavrakis, they aren't there for you to—to prod about like a boy poking at a crab with a stick!'

'I'm obviously getting under your skin,' he drawled. 'I'm proving that you do have feelings that haven't yet become desiccated.'

'This is just a game to you,' she said shakily. 'When I saw you for the first time in Reverend Mother's office I—I thought you could be cruel.'

'Cruel?' he exclaimed. 'You foolish child, you'll be cruel to yourself if you condemn yourself to a walled-up life. You are far too young to know your own mind!'

'So you presume to know it for me?'

'I presume to say that you shouldn't rule love out of your life until you have given yourself a chance to feel it. Everyone is entitled to fall in love at least once in a lifetime ... it can be overwhelming.'

Iris gazed at him wordlessly, wondering how they had got around to discussing such an intimate subject. She wanted, then, to seem as cool as the white dress she was wearing, but she felt a kind of heat sweeping up over her skin and could only pray that it wasn't visible to his keen eyes.

'Are you not curious about the sensual, mysterious conflict known as love?' he murmured, his eyes half veiled by cigar smoke as he rested them intently upon her face.

'Y-you have no right to ask me such a thing, Mr Mavrakis, and you know it——'

'While I pay for your services, Miss Ardath, I regard myself as having the right to converse with you, and that is what we are doing.'

'You ask questions and I'm expected to answer them. You're curious about me because I'm going to be a nun. I don't suppose I'd be of any interest to you if it wasn't for that. I have none of the glamour that you like.'

'Glamour comes out of pots and tubes and is painted on,' he drawled. 'You're being rather presumptuous when you say I like it. The two most intriguing women I have known were not women who painted and paraded and needed men to admire them. Their warmth and reality lay in their ability to love a man beyond themselves. Could you do that?'

'I—it's something I mustn't even think about,' she gasped.

'The things that go on inside one's head can be disturbing, can't they?'

She glanced away from his disturbing gaze ... the

entire man could play upon her nerves in a way that made her feel defenceless. She wanted him to behave like a conventional employer who treated her with a casual politeness; he really had no right to probe into the privacy of her thoughts, least of all those concerned with her future at St Clare's.

'Don't you think I should be taking Aleko home, sir?' Iris started to rise from her chair.

'Sit down and relax.' He waved her back into the chair. 'Aleko has gone off to sleep and is perfectly all right where he is. You are just dying to get away from me, aren't you?'

'You ask too many questions, sir, and then exert your authority in order to make me answer them.'

'The Greeks take a natural interest in other people; they haven't the reserve of the British.'

'Because we are reserved, Mr Mavrakis, we resent curiosity about our private lives.'

'I'm aware of that. My brother has an English wife and I'm acquainted with this reserve which affects some women to such a degree that they endure emotional pain and fear without a murmur of protest. To be a Greek is to be in touch with the earthy aspects of life and I have little patience with the Jesuits who teach that self-denial is the way to heaven.' He flicked ash from his cigar and his eyes seemed to penetrate Iris. 'I know there are other ways.'

Iris caught her breath at the implication in his words. 'It wouldn't do for everyone to be takers,' she protested, 'some have to be givers.'

'And you are one of those, eh?'

'I like to think so.'

'Miss Goody-Two-Shoes, only those shoes they gave you to wear were instruments of torture. Is that all part of the training, to give the novices corns on their toes?'

'St Clare's depends for its support on charity, so we can't expect to be given fashion shoes to wear. It was wrong of you, Mr Mavrakis, to tell the woman in the shop to throw my things away.'

'I shall have to compensate by sending St Clare's a nice fat cheque, shan't I?'

'You think that money can buy everything——'

'It can buy a great deal, young woman. The Mavrakis brothers don't spend all theirs on wine, women and song. We plough a lot of our profits back into new ventures so people can be given work. Our reason for taking over this hotel was to keep it functioning; it is rather splendid but needs a large staff to run it. Its profit margin will never be a very good one, but it seemed such a pity that it should sink into obscurity and finally close its doors. Look at the length of this sun-lounge and the splendour of the ballroom beyond it. At around three-thirty when tea is served, a pianist will arrive to play upon that grand piano. The aura of this place belongs to the 'Twenties and the 'Thirties—it is like stepping back into time, and I mean to preserve its atmosphere.'

He lounged there, long legs stretched out, his gaze roaming lazily about the place. 'Fenella will like it,' he murmured.

'Is she very beautiful?' Iris found herself asking.

'Yes,' he nodded, 'in the way of a slim cool lily one might come across at the verge of a pool in a woodland. She's such a contrast to my brother that it's startling to see them together; he's the toughest Greek I've ever known.'

'Tougher than you?' Iris exclaimed. She couldn't

imagine anyone more decisive and overwhelming than Zonar Mavrakis.

'Wouldn't you credit me with at least a streak of tenderness?' he asked quizzically.

Iris thought of how he could be with Aleko ... she had seen the pair of them wrestling on the floor of the boy's bedroom, the boyish giggling and the man's laughter mingling together, that black hair in disarray on the broad brow. Yes, he might be vulnerable where Aleko was concerned. The older brother had no children.

'You have your moments, of course,' she said, her eyes skimming away from his, that strange feeling of breathlessness catching hold of her. In salvaging Aleko from the wreck which had killed his wife, Zonar had travelled along a dark corridor of emotional pain. The sorrow of it was still deep in his heart, in his marrow, feeding his memories with torn fragments of his love. Those lacerations of the heart had left their mark upon him ... she sensed in him a menace, a rage, a deeply repressed need to feel again what he had felt for his young Greek wife.

In one wrenching moment in the sun of Greece he had lost the joy and communion of true love; the sensual humour and deep-felt tenderness of being with his other self.

A strange, confounding upheaval went on inside Iris as she sat there gazing steadily out of the lounge windows, trying to look as if withdrawn from the man inside the tycoon. This compulsion to comfort him had to be clamped down; she couldn't give way to it like other women. For them there was no sin or sorrow in giving themselves to Zonar Mavrakis for the short time it took him to grow bored by his easy captivation of them. They clouded the white-hot memory that never really left him, and then with his cynical smile he paid them off with a jewel or a fur.

Iris knew this as surely as she saw the sun on the surface of the sea, winking there so vividly and yet doomed to fade as the day waned and darkness came down over the water.

'You're as deep as that sea, aren't you?'

She glanced at him, her eyes wide and reflective, their iris colour in vivid contrast to her white skin.

'I was thinking that the sea has a terrible kind of beauty.'

'Rather like love,' he murmured.

'I wouldn't know about that, sir.' She tried to say it airily.

'Of course you wouldn't.' His tone was lightly mocking. 'You are the original innocent, aren't you? No doubt the good sisters have taught you the rudiments but left unexplained that sometimes one human being reacts instinctively to another, just as a bee flies blindly to a scent in search of honey. Love is the honey.'

And the agony, she thought, as each of his words seemed to strike a separate nerve in her system. He had to be aware of his own dark power and magnetism, and it was as if he was beckoning her to fly blindly to him, knowing that she could be hurt more deeply than the worldly type of girl. What made him do this? Some instinct in him to have his revenge on the deity who had dealt so harshly with the girl he had loved?

Iris searched for the answer in his face, seeking it in his eyes, his strongly constructed jaw, and his mouth that was edged by an enigmatic smile. Even as he sat there, looking lazily at ease, he could be plotting to pull her down until not a fraction of her innocence was left. She'd be destroyed ... unable to return to St Clare's to take vows of chastity!

Silence crept like a draught along the lounge; it had emptied except for themselves and the picture windows dimmed as a bank of clouds rolled over the sun.

'Sometimes it's possible to feel the earth move, is it not?'

Iris gazed at him, so keenly uncertain of him that it showed in her eyes.

'Come, don't tell me you haven't felt this, or are your feet too far off the ground?'

'No, sir. I don't go around with my head in the clouds.'

'I detect a significant note in your voice, Miss Ardath. What are you trying to tell me?'

'I—I know from what happened to my own mother that—that people can hide cruelty behind their charm.'

'As the sea hides its sharks, eh?'

'Yes, if you want to put it that way, sir.'

'I've sailed the Greek waters and it's very easy to mistake a dolphin for a shark. They're both sleek and swift in the sea, except that one is a friend and the other a foe.'

Iris looked him straight in the eye. 'If you have trouble sorting out a killer fish from a friendly one, then you can imagine how I feel.'

His eyebrow elevated very slowly. 'You have decided that it isn't wise to get caught in my teeth, eh?'

'Is it, sir?'

Silently he ran his gaze over her. 'You have your nerve, young woman. How did it survive in that place?'

'With difficulty——' Then she caught her breath as she realised what she had admitted to him, that any show of temperament was frowned upon at the convent, and charity pupils such as herself were expected to be quiet, grateful and submissive.

'So the meek little nun has a rebel hiding inside her?' he mocked softly.

'It's you——' her cheeks stung hotly. 'You make me answer back——'

'And quick answers, miss, carry more truth than calculated ones.'

It was true and she couldn't deny it; there had been rebellious times when she had wanted to ask why her hands were plunged into a sink full of greasy dishwater more often than the hands of her friend Colette. And why was it that she was always helping in the laundry room while the French girl was enlisted to pick peas in the garden or apples in the orchard?

In her heart Iris knew the answer ... even the devout had to pick and choose between the pauper and the princess; it was, after all, the paying pupil who made it possible for St Clare's to take in the charity child. Sometimes in the night Iris had awoken to find she had been weeping in her sleep; she had called herself a little fool, but now she realised that unconsciously she had wept at the unfairness of life. It seemed that if you already had someone to love you, then others loved you as well. But if you had no one who cared, then you were overlooked as a person and were treated almost as an abstraction. Duty was expected of you, not the gaiety and charm of someone like Colette. You washed the dishes and ironed the pinafores; you peeled the vegetables and waited on the tables: you fell into bed aching with tiredness and heard as in a dream the sound of someone sobbing. You woke startled and found the tears were your own.

Iris sat there lost in her thoughts and the time between luncheon and teatime must have passed, because a piano was playing a rather sweet tune she hadn't heard before, and there was a tinkle of teacups and spoons, and the sound of voices. The clouds had drifted away and the sun was shining again, a deeper tinge to its gold.

Iris lifted startled eyes when Zonar Mavrakis suddenly rose to his feet, surging tall and dark above her. She glanced up at him, but he wasn't looking at her, his gaze was fixed upon someone who had entered the lounge through one of the archways.

'Are you not pleased,' enquired a gay young voice, 'to see your *jolie laide* again?'

The voice struck a chord in Iris ... warm, self-assured, and with a French accent.

She turned to look, and unbelievably Colette Morel had emerged from her thoughts to become a reality. Her hair tumbled to her shoulders in soft disarray, a shade more honey than the beige fur slung casually around the shoulders of a copper chiffon dress. She held out an elegant hand with softly shining fingernails, extending it to Zonar Mavrakis.

'*Dieu*, to look again into those deep, dark, brooding Greek eyes! They remember me, I can see that!'

'By the gods,' amusement curled on his mouth, 'what on earth are you doing here?'

'I've come to stay, *mon ami*.' Colette approached him, and still she hadn't noticed Iris, who felt as if locked into the curled rattan of her chair.

'Here at the Monarch?'

'I heard the Mavrakis brothers had bought it, from a modelling friend of mine. I made a few discreet enquiries.' The elegant hand lost itself in the large hand; the charming face was raised for his kiss, and Iris watched dumbly as Zonar bent his tall head and laid his lips against the rounded cheekbone. Something inside stabbed at Iris ... a pointed little arrow reminding her that Colette had always found it easy to get what she wanted.

CHAPTER FIVE

THE garden of the villa was exceptionally attractive and Iris liked wandering there when she had a little time to herself. She and Aleko had been for a boat trip and now he was pretending to be a sailor by taking his nap in a hammock the manservant had slung between a pair of trees.

Iris smiled a little to herself as she wandered the paths that meandered through the garden, sloped and stepped so that views of the sea could be taken in at most angles. Aleko was an amusing and inventive child and daily she grew more attached to him ... it would be a wrench for her when the time came for them to part, but right now the moment had a quiet restfulness, and the summer wouldn't end just yet.

She wandered down into a mass of azaleas, some of them a gorgeous peach colour, mingling with the deeper hues of rhododendrons. Hardly any scent she noticed, but the colours made up for that. She passed beneath the trailing branches of a huge elm tree which enclosed a small gazebo, where she sometimes sat and read. She had found a wide selection of books in the library of the villa, some of them so highly romantic that it amused her to bring them here so she could read about this emotion which had been kept so rigorously out of her life. She found them curiously absorbing, and realised almost at once that they weren't personal to the man who had leased the villa for the summer. They belonged to the owner, a widow who left England each year at this time to stay with her daughter in Florence. A lonely woman, Iris thought, who found a certain consolation in her collection of highly imaginative fiction. In was only fiction. In real life nobody fell in love so passionately as the people in the books. Iris read them rather guiltily, for they weren't the type of books approved of by Reverend Mother. She would have advised Iris not to believe a word of such high-flown nonsense.

Iris paused to let her gaze dwell upon a bank of golden daisies and bright blue bells; she could hear a bee buzzing among the flowers, where he would smother himself in pollen and carry away to the hive the nectar for the honeycomb.

Love is the honey ... the words drifted through her mind. Her employer had spoken them that significant day at the hotel, when out of the blue Colette had re-entered both their lives. Even yet Iris could feel a jolt of amazement ... she hadn't dreamed that her path would ever cross Colette's again. When they had parted at the convent it had seemed inevitable that they would go their different ways, Colette into the world of fashion which had always beckoned her, while Iris became closer drawn into a world where adornment of the body was not approved.

Iris reached out to fondle the lovely creamy head of a rhododendron that swayed towards her. The petals were soft to her touch and she was moved to a sense of wonderment at the perfection of the flowers; a big brown bee snuggled his body deep into a mauve flower and she heard him buzzing there, busily at work powdering himself with golden dust. Iris couldn't imagine what it must be like to model dresses and parade for the customers as Colette did. But she had seen for herself that the French girl had grown up into the kind of sophisticated woman Zonar Mavrakis would find attractive.

She was one of the *cabine des mannequins* at Gil Patrice, which had recently opened a branch in London. 'I had a holiday due to me, *chéri*.' She had trailed her shining fingernails down the lean hardness of his jaw. 'I thought I would come and spend it at your hotel—and what a very chic place it is, *mon ami*, perched on its hilltop like the sun-palace of Apollo!'

Colette had gazed up into his eyes and smiled the impudent smile Iris remembered so well; time and again it had won her a reprieve while Iris ended up in the kitchen with a pile of dishes to wash.

So absorbed by the man, Colette hadn't noticed Iris, and when Colette had looked at her, slanting eyes sharpening with surprise, there had been a sense of restraint between them rather than the delight of old friends meeting again.

'What on earth are you doing here?' Colette exclaimed, looking Iris up and down to make sure it was her. 'And why are you dressed like that—didn't you take your vows?'

If Iris had hoped for a renewal of the old friendship, her hopes had crashed like the waves on the seashore rocks. She realised at once that she and Colette had always been worlds apart; she smiled, but it hurt as she cut the memories adrift.

The two of them were now adult and there had been a wary, inquisitive gleam in the French girl's eyes. 'Don't tell me,' she said, 'that you have been allowed out of St Clare's without a chaperone? Is that not daring ... there are men about!'

She had laughed and allowed her fur to drift casually apart so the charm of her figure was more apparent to the man who stood looking quizzically from one girl to the other. 'We knew each other at St Clare's,' Colette explained. 'Iris was always very prim and proper, but funnily enough she always ended up being the one who got scolded. I used to tell her that it paid to be naughty because the penalty for being good is always more severe. I couldn't leave the place quickly enough! Just try to imagine *me* as a nun!'

She took a mannequin pose in front of him and smiled into his eyes. He quirked an eyebrow and beckoned a waitress. 'Come, you must join us for tea,' he told Colette. 'It is now a rule here at the Monarch that the cucumber sandwiches are always crisp, the cakes freshly made, and the piano music never modern.'

Colette sank gracefully down in an armchair, while Iris was conscious of sitting tensely in her own chair. She felt a sense of intrusion ... something indefinable in Colette's manner made her feel like a servant. She wanted to leave Zonar alone with his guest, but Aleko was curled up so snugly in the window-seat, sound asleep and unaware that the girl in Paris had materialised here at the Monarch.

A breeze rustled through the garden and a sweet-sharp scent of the sea wafted to Iris. She pushed a hand over her short sleek hair, in which the sun found streaks of amber. She wore a shirt casually open at the neck, and a brown doeskin skirt. Her feet were encased in a pair of the new sandals and her browning legs were bare. Across the bay a glow of colour was gathering around the sun. The long line of cliffs snaked along until they were lost in the distance. She loved the beauty and melancholy of late afternoon, and the way the gulls flew and cried around the rocks. For a while she felt tranquil and relaxed and free of the strange tension which affected her up at the villa.

She gave quite a start when she heard a footfall on the path behind her; she swung round and there was Colette, looking rather out of place in this informal garden in an off-white suit and scarlet blouse, Chanel C's on her handbag and the corner of the chiffon scarf tied elegantly to protect her hair from the sea breezes. Her lips had a luscious gloss to them, and they curled into a smile as her gaze flicked Iris from head to toe.

'You don't seem to get any older,' she said. 'Don't you ever wear a dab of make-up to take off the schoolgirlish shine?'

'It never occurs to me,' Iris admitted. 'I wouldn't know how to apply it, and Reverend Mother would hardly approve.'

'How is she keeping?' Colette drawled. 'I could always twist her around my finger, but I suppose in my case she knew it was a waste of time to try and reserve me for better things.'

'She's very well.' Iris smiled slightly. 'You were always a favourite of hers. You livened up the place.'

'So I did, *chérie*.' Colette glanced around her, wrinkling her finely plucked eyebrows. 'I hope there aren't any gnats about. I don't want to be bitten—are you not bothered, strolling here with bare legs and arms? Your skin is very pale and that is the kind they bite, eh?'

'I apply a repellent. I found when I first came here that I was inclined to get bitten and the bites did sting and swell, so the *kyrios* suggested that I buy some rather good gel at Boots, down by the harbour. It works, thank heaven!'

'The *kyrios*?' That inquisitive look came into Colette's slanting eyes; pale brown eyes with a tinge of green, above which the lashes and brows were skilfully darkened with mascara. 'Are you referring to Zonar? Is that what you call him?'

'Yes.' Iris found it a little startling to see her one-time convent friend wearing make-up. Scrubbed faces were the rule at St Clare's. 'It means "master" in Greek. After all, I work for him, and it seems to suit him.'

'Yes, he is very masterful.' The slanting eyes had narrowed and the green in them seemed to glint through the dark lashes. 'Do you find him thrilling, Iris?'

'W-what do you mean?' Iris felt her heart give an erratic beat.

'Chérie, you are not that innocent!' Colette gave a scornful laugh. 'You are well aware of what I mean. You live in his house and you see him often—you must have noticed it.'

'Notice what?'

'His nerve, devil-arrogance, damn you to hell and heaven!'

'Ah—that!'

'Dieu!' Colette cast her eyes heavenwards. 'I know you plan to take the veil, but don't tell me you can live in the same house with that Greek and feel angelic all the time? Those eyes of his turn my knees to water! I could fall into them and drown! I just had to see him again, and then when I saw you with him—for the moment I wondered if he had married you!'

'How absurd!' Iris retreated as if from a blow, unaware that the path behind her had dwindled to the edge of the cliffs. Her slim figure was outlined against the tinge of rose in the sky and there was a defensive look about her.

'Of course it's absurd.' Colette laughed gaily. 'But he

thinks so much of the child that he might well take a wife for the sake of Aleko, rather than consider his own feelings. Greeks have strong feelings towards their sons and will do almost anything for them.'

'To the extent of—of marrying someone like me in order to provide him with a mother?' Iris spoke drily. 'I would say that Mr Mavrakis is not that hard up for a selection of women to choose from—I would place myself at the very bottom of the list of candidates.'

'So would I, *chérie*,' Colette agreed. 'You are not his type at all, but it was seeing you there, in his company. For a crazy moment it flashed across my mind that he might have married you—I mean, you aren't the sort to interfere in a man's life, or to impose yourself in any way. Aleko would have a mother, but Zonar would still be emotionally free to——' Colette broke off with a meaningful laugh. 'You take my meaning, eh?'

'You refer to a wife in name only,' Iris said quietly. 'A marriage of convenience, I believe it's called.'

'That is exactly what it is called.' Colette looked amazed that Iris should know such a thing. 'In a way not unlike taking the veil and becoming an untouched bride—that's what you have always wanted, is it not?'

'I'm not going to discuss it,' Iris replied. 'Nor this other nonsense—Mr Mavrakis has employed me to take care of Aleko for a few weeks, so there's no need for you to concern yourself, Colette, with the idea that there is anything remotely matrimonial in his mind.'

'What is in your mind, I wonder?' Colette opened her handbag and drew out a slim gold case, from which she took a cheroot. 'I don't imagine that you have taken up smoking, eh?'

Iris shook her head, watching the painted flicker of Colette's finger nails as she thumbed her lighter and bent her head to the flame. As she emitted smoke from her nostrils her eyes met and held Iris's. 'You were always a deep one—the suffering kind, eh? Even if Zonar Mavrakis did stir you up, you would sooner burn at the stake than admit it. As I used to say to you even when we were schoolgirls together, I couldn't endure a life deprived of a man's arms around me. *Dieu*, if there is a heaven on earth it is in a pair of strong arms, beneath lips that crush and burn and whisper mad things. How can you possibly cut out of your life such a thrilling experience? Are you not curious about it?'

The breeze across the bay blew cool upon Iris's skin and for a moment she had a mental image of Zonar Mavrakis as she had seen him early one morning, coming up from the beach after a swim, wearing nothing more than a pair of sun-bleached trousers belted against a flat brown midriff, his black hair damp and tousled on his brow. She had stood very still, almost unbreathing as he strolled past the grove of trees where she was, but she had been intensely aware of his supple grace of movement, his air of controlled physical power, and because he carried only a towel she had guessed that he swam in the sea naked and was probably a deep brown from his head to his heels.

As Colette realised, it wasn't possible to live in the same house as Zonar and not be aware of him as a man, but this awareness was Iris's secret and nothing would have torn it from her. Colette was the last person she would tell; they weren't schoolroom chums any longer, and the French girl was infatuated by him.

'It's best if you don't rack your brains trying to figure me out,' Iris said lightly. 'You and I were always opposites.'

'And opposites attract, so it is said.' Colette blew

smoke from her glossy lips, but the sharp glint of green was apparent in her eyes. 'You have lived like a nun, and though Zonar has been a widower for nine years he hasn't lived as a monk. The situation is piquant, *non*? You can understand my curiosity?'

'You were always inquisitive,' Iris agreed. 'I could see it came as a surprise to you, seeing me with the man you had met in Paris——'

'Paris,' Colette sighed. 'There is no city in the world more romantic, and there he took me dancing and took me home as dawn was breaking over the Seine. I sensed that he felt something for me, but he's wary, like a tiger that fears the trap.' Colette blew smoke towards Iris and smiled narrowly. 'He's the kind of man I have been searching for. The Mavrakis brothers are a formidable trio and it was from the wife of Demi Mavrakis that I picked up the piece of information which led me here—she is highly fashionable and spends lavishly on her clothes.'

Colette glanced down at herself, studying her shoes, her sheer hose and the fit of her skirt. 'At Gil Patrice they treated her as if she were royalty. She has a certain chic, but she is no great beauty. Dressed in the kind of clothes she can afford I could outshine her very easily. She has that dark skin which is so attractive in a man but not so good in a woman.'

'I understand that the older brother's wife is very beautiful,' Iris said, with a touch of mischief.

'So?' Colette shrugged her shoulders. 'If he is over forty, then she is probably as old.'

'I understand that she's younger than he, and very fair to look at.'

'Zonar discusses his family with you—you, a governess?'

'He did happen to mention his brother Lion has an English wife.'

'And when do you have these domestic conversations?'

'Usually when Aleko has gone to bed.'

'How cosy!' Colette stared at Iris in silhouette against the sunset, on this wedge of private cliff. The sky across the water was like a sheet of fire-red satin, with threads of gold torn from it. In the lengthening shadows and the quivering of leaves Iris had a subtle look of being part of the scene.

'It must make your day,' Colette drawled, 'waiting for him to arrive home so you can be alone with him—and don't tell me you sit there like a nun when he looks at you with those Grecian eyes and speaks to you in that deep gritty voice—and maybe touches you!'

'I don't let him touch me!'

'He wouldn't ask permission, *chérie*. The Mavrakis men are takers—they say that once burned by a Greek's passion a women never feels warm again in the arms of other men.' Colette took a sudden step forward. 'What has really been going on, eh? Is it anything Reverend Mother would not care to be told?'

The sea was sheened by the blaze of the westering sun, and then as it sank away a violet-tinged melancholy crept over the clifftop garden. A breeze rustled through the trees and the scents of the flowers were suddenly stronger.

Iris stood there feeling strangely threatened ... it was absurd to feel so nervous of someone who had been her friend, but Colette looked as if she wanted to claw out her eyes. Instinctively she took a step backwards and the next moment was falling through space and grappling wildly for a hold on something—anything that would stop her from plunging all the way down in the dark, to where the sea was riding in over the rocks.

The skin of her hands felt ripped and her very bones felt as if they'd come loose from their sockets as she grasped a shrubby branch jutting from the cliffside, jarring every nerve in her body as she stopped falling and hung there, holding on desperately with her abraded hands. *Dear God!* She gasped the words aloud as her heart thudded with shock and fear. *Help me!*

Her dangling feet sought for a foothold, grazing themselves against the hard surface of the cliffs. Unless she could ease her weight on the branch it could tear loose from the rock in which it was embedded and she'd smash on those rocks below like an egg dropped from a bird's nest. A cold sweat filmed her body ... how long would it take Colette to fetch help? Already the ligaments of her arms felt stretched and burning, and in her efforts to attach her feet to some kind of projection she was almost breaking her toes.

Time seemed to have no meaning as the painful seconds crawled by, then by straining her body she managed to support her feet on a rough sill of rock. This eased just a little the strain on her arms and neck, but she could feel her strength gradually ebbing away and realised that she couldn't hold on much longer.

She could hear the sea below her, splashing hungrily over the rocks in the gathering darkness. 'Holy Mother of God....' she breathed, and tried not to imagine what it would feel like if she fell. A shudder swept through her and she clung even more desperately to the shrub, which at any moment could tear free of the cliffside.

'IRIS!' The voice struck loud and imperative through the dusk. 'Hold on, girl, I am coming for you!'

'I'm holding on,' she gasped, 'just about....'

Way above her she caught the sound of other voices and suddenly a bright spotlight was spraying the cliffs, outlining her figure suspended there like a bird in a trap, her heart thudding as she waited to be hauled to safety.

A rope ladder was lowered and someone came climbing down to where she hung in the spotlight. A powerful arm hooked itself around her and a voice spoke urgently. 'I have you! Come, you don't have to be afraid any more!'

But her hands were clenched so tightly around the strands of the shrub that it hurt unlocking them; she still felt she might fall, but Zonar Mavrakis had hold of her and together they were hauled up the cliff and over the rim. Iris was dimly aware of people around them, of being wrapped in a blanket, of feeling the tang of cognac on her lips and the solid feel of the ground under her shaking legs and bruised feet.

'By the gods,' Zonar was standing over her, his eyes glittering in the glow of the hand lamps, 'someone up in that sky loves you!'

She gazed up at him, still too shaken for speech. Her eyes looked enormous in the pallor of her face, and though she wanted to thank him for coming to her rescue she couldn't seem to form the words. It was as if her mind and her senses still couldn't believe she was safe. In a sudden wave it swept over her that she had narrowly escaped being killed ... tears of reaction welled up in her eyes and with an exclamation in Greek her employer swung her up into his arms and the next moment was striding with her through the garden to the house. Wearied and aching, Iris was vaguely aware that someone called his name and followed them into the villa.

Up the stairs he strode with her, into her bedroom and through to the bathroom where steam was rising from the tub and a maid was waiting. He stood a moment holding her and looking down at her tear-streaked face.

'How did that come to happen?' he demanded.

'It just—happened.' Held by his eyes, and his arms, she felt helpless. He seemed angry and yet concerned and her stomach muscles fluttered.

'You are supposed to be my son's capable governess and you do an idiot thing like falling over the cliffs!' His eyes raked over her. 'What if Aleko had been with you?'

His angry concern was now explained and mutely she lowered her gaze.

'Little fool, be more careful in future.' He lowered her to her feet and she felt his arms unclose from around her. He told the maid to take care of her; her dinner would be brought to her in bed. In the doorway he glanced back at Iris. His black brows were drawn together as he looked at her; he was in his shirt sleeves, having abandoned tie and jacket. He looked very dark and big against the pastels of the bathroom.

'Are you hurt in any way?' he demanded. 'Bruised?'

'Not seriously,' she replied. There was a strange aching somewhere in the region of her ribs; she couldn't talk about it because it seemed unrelated to her fall. 'I—I shall soon mend—thank you for what you did.'

'Thank Colette,' he said, rather brusquely. Hearing the mention of her name the French girl came to his side and stood there close to him in the doorway, gazing at Iris limpidly.

'I was petrified, *chérie*.' Her fingers curled around Zonar's arm, just below where his sleeve was rolled up, her fingernails like ovals of flame against his brown skin. 'I felt sure you must be killed.'

'Someone loves her,' Zonar growled. 'Come, let's leave her to soak the strain out of her body.'

The next moment they were gone, Colette talking animatedly as they went, and Iris submitted to the attentions of the young maid. Once she was in the bath, however, she wanted to be left on her own. 'Then I'll go and see about your dinner tray, miss.' The girl eyed Iris's shirt and skirt, which had been ripped and dirtied by her fall. 'We can get the skirt cleaned for you, miss, but just look at your shirt, all ripped under the sleeves.'

'I should like the skirt cleaned, but don't worry about the shirt.' Iris eased her body down in the warm bubbly water and leaned her head against the rubber headrest ... mmm, that felt better!

'It must have been awful, miss.' There was an awe-struck note in the girl's voice. 'Just like a film ... what with Mr Mavrakis climbing down like that to fetch you to safety. You must have been scared stiff!'

'I was.' A slight smile etched itself about Iris's lips. 'I could hear the sea below me and my arms felt as if they were being pulled from their sockets. I'm still shaking inside. I don't really know if I can face any food.'

'I should have a try if I was you, miss. It's lamb chops with potatoes baked in their jackets, and pears and cream afterwards. I'm sure you could manage some of that.'

'I—I expect so.' Iris sighed and moved her sore toes in the water. The bathroom door closed behind the girl and it was a relief to be left on her own to soak not only the soreness but the residue of terror out of herself.

She let her thoughts roam over the incident and it struck her that Colette must have seen how close she was to the edge of the cliffs, yet she hadn't warned her as most people would have done. She hadn't said: 'Watch out or you'll fall!'

Iris faced the truth, absurd as it seemed. Colette saw her as a rival for Zonar Mavrakis' affections, and the fact that he had climbed down the cliffs himself in order to bring her to safety would add fuel to the jealous fire burning in the French girl. Because she was self-centred it wouldn't occur to her that Zonar would always take charge in the event of a crisis and face personally whatever danger was involved. He hadn't risked his neck because his son's governess was anyone special ... he had called her a little idiot, and there hadn't been much sympathy in his voice when he had asked if she was bruised.

Iris splashed water over her arms and dreaded to to think what they would feel like in the morning. And try as she might she couldn't seem to thrust from her mind the image of herself clinging for dear life to the shrub growing out of the cliff-face. Even as Zonar had climbed down after her, she had felt herself weakening ... almost in the nick of time he had thrust his muscular arm around her, forcefully taking charge of her, and re-charging her with his own energy.

Now she felt drained, but she was alive and despite her aches and the vivid marks of bruises against her pale skin she was in one piece ... would she need to inform Reverend Mother of the occurrence? If she did so she might be ordered back to St Clare's, and as her gaze slid around the comfort of the bathroom Iris realised that she didn't want to return to the convent until she had to.

She bit her lip guiltily, for it felt like a transgression to admit to herself that she liked bathing in this deep tub without being hampered by the cotton shift the girls were obliged to wear when they took a bath at St Clare's. There were no mirrors on the walls, no heated rails where snowy Turkish towels waited warm and enveloping, no springy matting on the floor, fat bars of Pears' soap and pot-bellied jars of bath crystals. She had often had to share the lukewarm water after a paying pupil had bathed in the narrow white tub, and the towel would be damp from having been used already.

Iris tried not to make such comparisons, but they seemed to invade her mind before she could reject them. Even as she lay here in the soft, scented water she could see herself in one of the wall mirrors; the pallor of her shoulders, the damp tendrils of hair against her neck, the wonderment in her own eyes.

She had come to Tormont in all innocence, but now she was wondering if it was possible for her to return to the convent in the same state of mind. She could no longer ignore the fact that the master of the villa had a force and a fascination she hadn't dreamed of, shut away behind stone walls among a group of devout women who had forsworn the company of men. Only an hour ago she had been held to his hard body and had felt the supple movement of his muscles when he had climbed the cliffs supporting her, and handling her.

A hand crept to her breast and her lips opened as if with a silent plea ... she saw her own vulnerability and look of alarm in her eyes....

'Oh——' She swung a look at the door as it suddenly opened and Aleko wandered in. Unaccustomed to locking doors at the convent, where it was forbidden, Iris never thought to do so here at the villa. Seeing the boy standing there, she gasped and clutched the sponge to her.

'Aleko, you mustn't come in here!'

'Why not?' he asked reasonably. 'I do so when Papa is in the bath or the shower.'

'That's different, he's your father. I——'

'You have very white skin, haven't you?' He wandered over to the side of the tub and gazed at her inquisitively. 'Papa is very brown and he has black hairs on his chest and arms. You haven't any hairs on your arms, but what are those black marks? Louise told me you fell over the cliffs and Papa had to go down after you. Is it true?'

'Yes, but now it's all over. Now please go out of the bathroom, Aleko. I have to get dressed.' She had forgotten for the moment that her employer had ordered her into bed as soon as she had bathed.

'I don't mind staying.' He sat down on the bath stool and looked at her with those dark eyes that were disturbingly like his father's, very Greek and with a subtle slant to them, with thick lashes that seemed to weigh on the lids.

'I do mind you staying,' she said indignantly. 'When people take a bath they're entitled to their privacy, so get up from that stool and march yourself out of here this instant!'

'Do I make you feel shy, then?' he enquired. 'I know that girls are different from boys, so don't let it worry you.'

'Really——!' For a moment she was speechless, and then all at once her sense of humour overcame her modesty and she started to laugh. 'Go away, you little wretch! You know you shouldn't be in here——'

There she broke off, for someone else had poked his head around the door and this time the eyes weren't boyish. 'So there you are, young man! Miss Ardath at her ablutions isn't a sideshow for your enjoyment.'

This time Iris slid down in the water as far as she could get without drowning. 'You Greeks!' she gasped. 'I thought you had some respect for the proprieties!'

'We do, *thespoinis*.' But even as he said it, he was entering the bathroom and scooping Aleko off the stool. He swung his highly amused son upon the wide shoulders in black suiting. The shirt beneath was pale-grey silk and a tie of darker grey was impeccably knotted ... he looked ready for an evening on the town.

'You are now looking less pallid,' he said.

She knew her face was flushed as the turbulent blood beat through her veins ... he had to realise that this was the first time in her life that a man had seen her in the bath, and because the bubbles were beginning to evaporate he couldn't help but see the shape of her in the water.

'The water's getting cold,' she said desperately. 'I—I want to get out, so would you mind leaving a-and taking your offspring with you?'

'Yes, I think we had better depart, my son, before your governess succeeds in drowning herself—either in water or confusion.' Laughing in that soft, mocking way of his, Zonar carried his son out of the bathroom, leaving Iris to scramble out of the tub as fast as her aching arms and legs would allow. She grabbed one of the large towels and enveloped herself in its folds—her cheeks still stung and the pupils of her eyes were widely expanded.

Hastily she dried herself, but when she glanced

around for something to put on she realised that the maid had taken away all her clothes and forgotten to bring in her dressing-gown from the bedroom. Taking a deep breath, Iris tightened the towel around her and entered her bedroom, a sigh of relief escaping her when she found it was empty. Her robe lay across one of the bedroom chairs and she was reaching for it when, again without knocking, the door was thrust open to admit Zonar Mavrakis.

He was alone and he wasn't smiling. He closed the door behind him, almost deliberately it seemed, and came towards Iris. A shuddering little tremor ran through her, for his eyes were probing her bare shoulders and arms.

'I beg of you not to look at me as if I'm about to rape you,' he said.

'W-what do you want——?'

'I want to see how bruised you are. Aleko told me there were dark marks on your skin, probably more noticeable because your skin is so white and the boy is more used to seeing my tough hide.' Abruptly as he spoke Zonar reached out and drew the towel away from her upper arms; he stared down intently at her and she cringed, self-consciously, when he traced with a fingertip the bruising at the top of her left arm where she had hit against the cliff-face in her struggles to maintain her hold on the shrub.

She heard Zonar pull in his breath. 'Are there more like this?' he demanded. 'Come, you don't have to be shy with me!'

But she felt intensely shy of him; his touch sent a tingling sensation through her very bones and she felt as if her legs were going to fold in half.

'Please—they'll fade away in a day or two——'

'Show me,' he insisted. 'You know I can make you, if I have to.'

'T-there are one or two on my legs——'

'And elsewhere?'

'I—I was bound to get bruised. Please, it isn't anything to worry about. I'm lucky to be alive.'

'Assuredly,' he agreed. 'But if you have any bad abrasions, then they must be attended to in case they become infected. I insist that you show me so I can judge for myself.'

'No——' Iris backed away from him, unmindful that he was holding part of the towel and that her movement would dislodge it completely. It fell away from her and to her mortification she was uncovered from head to heel and here was no way to hide herself from the almost merciless look that Zonar swept over her.

'By the gods,' he muttered, 'you took quite a battering against those cliffs, didn't you? And you weren't going to say a word. You were going to suffer in silence.'

'Don't—please don't look at me!' She grabbed at her robe and was shaking as she fumbled with it. Somehow she got it on, a flush across her cheeks as she tied the sash in a secure knot.

'You little fool!'

'Of course.' She flung back the hair from her brow. 'When you came to St Clare's to hire a governess, Colette had already left!'

'Why bring Colette into the conversation?' he asked sardonically.

'For the simple reason that she wouldn't be foolish enough to fall over the cliffside. She believes in self-preservation.'

'Most people do—and there really is no need to tie

yet another knot in the sash of your robe. I've got the message, you know.'

She glanced at him before she could stop herself and saw the derisive little smile on the edge of his mouth.

'You shouldn't be ashamed of your body,' he drawled.

'I'm not,' she denied, but she found her gaze fixed upon the smoked-pearl pin in his tie; she just had to avoid those dark eyes which had seen her as no one else had done, not since she was a young child who needed someone to bathe her. Her bare skin felt visible through the folds of her robe and she felt an aching sense of torment, as if she wanted to cry, but not in front of him.

'Your bruises will need an application of witch-hazel,' he said. 'Will you do it yourself——'

'Yes,' she broke in.

'Yes,' he mocked. 'I was going to suggest that Louise the maid do it for you, in case you were leaping to the conclusion that I wanted the job. A bottle of the stuff is kept in my bedroom cabinet for use on Aleko when he takes a tumble, so I'll go and fetch it and suggest in the meantime that you sit down before you fall down. I can see you trembling from here!'

He swung on his heel and strode from her bedroom and much as she wanted to dash over and bolt the door on his return, she didn't really have the stamina or the nerve. Reaction from her misadventure was setting in and she sank faintly into a nearby chair and leaned weakly forward with her head down over her knees. She clung to the arms of the chair for the room seemed to be going around ... oh lord, she hadn't felt so close to fainting since Asian 'flu had swept through the convent and she had contracted it while helping to nurse some of the infants who had gone down with it.

She was drooping there when Zonar returned and hadn't the strength to resist when he slid an arm around her and held the rim of a glass to her lips. She tasted the spirit and managed to swallow it. She took a deep breath and the faintness began to recede.

'Are you feeling less fragile?'

She looked into his eyes, but they weren't mocking her. They held a look of concern which almost gave her a fresh attack of the faintness. 'I it all swept over me, but I'm all right now, thank you.'

'Other women might have thrown a fit of hysterics—come, drink a little more of the whisky; it's Chevas Regal and good for you. You were admirably stoic for someone suspended above razor-sharp rocks. They'd have cut you to ribbons, or didn't you realise it?'

She shuddered, remembering the sound of the sea splashing over those rocks.

'It doesn't hurt for a woman to give way to her emotions.' He sat on the side of the bed and his left eyebrow took a slanting angle. 'You hold yours in at all cost, don't you? You hate to be caught with your defences down. Colette would have screamed blue murder.'

'I'm not Colette,' she murmured, and she gazed at him with deep-blue, shadowy eyes. 'She never did bother to learn self-discipline.'

'There are times when it's to hell with self-discipline.' He snapped his fingers dismissively. 'You clamped down your feelings and they got back at you and you almost passed out just now. Has the room stopped going around?'

She looked at him with surprise; how would he know, a man so big, strong and sure, what it felt like to feel on the verge of a swoon? She nodded.

'Don't look at me with such eyes.' He tossed back the

remainder of the whisky. 'It used to happen to my wife when she first became pregnant with Aleko. I know all about women, Miss Ardath, though I can't say that any man ever fully plumbs their mystery. What does a girl of eighteen expect to get from religious ecstasy?'

Iris turned her head away, too aware of his maleness there on her bed to be sure of herself.

'Look at me!' His hand was suddenly clasping the nape of her neck and he was leaning over her, capturing her eyes. 'Shall I prove to you that you do have something in common with Colette?'

'I—I'm aware that we all have an animal instinct.' The pressure of his fingers against her neck was a warning that he could master her body very easily ... her heart raced at the mere thought of it.

'We also have a natural need for someone who will cherish our every hair and sinew, every inch of skin covering the cage in which we're ultimately so alone. No one can truly love himself as another can, with a rapture you will never find in your cool chapel among the images of saints and *angeli*. The incense there won't rise to your head like the wine of passion.'

As he spoke his hand moved against the soft side of her neck and she became intensely aware of how flimsy a barrier was the fabric of her robe. A residue of faintness passed over her. 'Please—no!' She didn't quite know what she was saying.

'That is a contradiction in terms.' His breath slid warm across her face as he drew closer, and her body stiffened as he arched her across his arm. She was silenced into shock as his mouth covered hers, taking her lips even as she opened them to plead ... to protest.

Unbelievably he was kissing her ... his mouth held hers and she could feel the hard pressure of his jaw, the play of his lips and the sound of his breathing. The intimacy of it was incredible to her. He had no right to be doing this to her, and with a convulsive movement she tried to break free of his grip.

As if her resistance made the deep-down savagery erupt in him, he swung her completely out of the chair and lowered her to the bed, thrusting her down upon it as he took a lounging position above her struggling body. He smiled at her ineffectual efforts to escape him.

'Is it the little nun who fights me?' he murmured. 'Or the woman who's afraid of what she might discover about herself?'

Her eyes raced over his face, more dark and devilish than ever before. 'Why can't you leave me alone?' she panted. 'Why do you keep on tormenting me?'

'You know why,' he breathed. 'You bring out the devil in me, and you felt it that first time at the convent when you walked in and looked at me as if Lucifer had been let into your safe little life. I knew exactly what was going on behind those eyes of yours ... you wanted to beg your Mother Superior to let you stay where you were, out of harm's way of a man like me.'

He laughed softly, holding her pinioned beneath him. 'You thought the convent doors had opened to let the devil in, didn't you?'

'Yes!' She glared up defiantly at him. 'I thought you the most arrogant person I'd ever seen. I could see what women meant to you—you think they are yours for the taking, but I'm not!'

'I could take you here and now,' he mocked. 'You wouldn't stand a chance.'

Her eyes widened ... widened to take in the ruthlessness she saw in his face. He had the strength to do as he pleased with her and it terrified her that what he did might be more of a pleasure than a sin.

'You—you wouldn't get anywhere near the real me!' she gasped.

'I touch you and you're real enough.' He slid a hand down the side of her neck to where her robe exposed the curve of her shoulder. 'Your skin is warm, yet you shiver——'

'You're being so hateful—you have no right to try and make me do wrong!'

'Would I have to try so hard?' He lowered his face until his mouth was against her neck. 'Come, give way to your feelings. Don't fight natural instinct, little one.'

'I despise you——' She twisted and turned in an effort to evade his warm invasive lips.

'Because I know you like it?' His lips teased her ear-lobe. 'A girl with skin as soft and sensitive as yours couldn't help but like having it touched.'

'I'd sooner have fallen over those cliffs than have you ouch me!' Words were her only weapon against the creeping langour that was more frightening than his trength. 'Do you think I owe you my body because you happened to save it?'

His hand where it cupped the curve of her shoulder grew suddenly still, burning through to her collarbone until abruptly he drew away from her. His face and voice had hardened. 'I don't take that sort of talk from nyone. I'm still your employer and don't you forget t!'

'You're the one who's forgetting it!' With a look of affronted dignity Iris adjusted her robe.

'You won't get a baby from just a kiss,' he said, with quiet insolence. 'In case you were wondering.'

She glanced away from him, her cheeks stinging. 'It's hat leads to it,' she muttered.

'I beg your pardon?' He leaned down to her mockingly. 'I didn't quite catch what you said, Miss Ardath.'

She sat there, her head lowered as the loneliness of having no one akin to her slid through her mind. 'I'm a St Clare's charity child, Mr Mavrakis. Does that answer your question satisfactorily?'

When he didn't answer she felt a compulsion to look up at him; his expression was curiously stern. 'Is that why you're determined to die a virgin?'

'I don't regard it as the most terrible thing that can happen,' she replied.

'Don't you?' His eyes swept her face. 'A Greek believes that a woman is made to yield like the olive tree, and there is no lovelier sight than the olive trees in fruit, no sadder sight than when they are gnarled and their leaves rattle in the wind like dry paper.'

'Do Greeks always speak in parables?' Iris strove not to think of the elderly nuns at St Clare's, with their gnarled fingers and bent spines from years of working the soil or bending over sickbeds. Their lives were devoted to serving others regardless of any reward, and Iris revered them but often felt in awe of their saintliness. They took service and suffering to their hearts as if it were a cross to which they nailed their secret dreams and unspoken desires.

Iris knew that Zonar Mavrakis was forcing her to face the pain when she drove the mythical nails through her own dreams and desires.

'We Greeks are realists,' he said, 'and yet in a way we are also romantics, for Greece is a land of contrasts. On my brother's island there are a million butterflies—did you know that they are blind and fly by scent alone?'

She shook her head almost bemusedly, for she hadn't

heard him speak like this before, nor had she seen that faraway look in his eyes, almost softening his expres-ion.

'In many ways love is blind,' he murmured. 'It omes from out of the dark recesses of ourselves, a park that seeks the air so it can burst into flame.' His yes dwelt upon her there on the bed. 'What if such a lame should come to life inside you, Miss Ardath? Fire sn't easy to quench once it starts to spread, and it may ave its way with you.'

'I shall do my utmost to avoid what might cause such spark,' she said determinedly.

'Really?' He gave a taunting little laugh. 'What if he damage is already done and deep inside you a spark already smouldering and seeking its outlet? These hings happen quickly, taking us unaware.'

'For that to happen, sir, I should need to meet a nan——' She broke off confusedly, for directly in front f her stood a man, potent with all the force which nade the male so opposite to the female; so mysterious, emanding and dangerous.

'I thought blushing had gone out of style,' he mur-nured. 'I'm not exactly a mouse, am I, miss?'

'More like a tiger!' The words had escaped before ne could restrain them, but in a curious way it was ue. He had the alertness, symmetry and ruthlessness f the tawny-coated tiger; he walked as a tiger walked .. he pounced as silently and as surely, and left his ark.

'You flatter me,' he drawled. 'Unless, of course, you ave in mind only the woman-eating side of the tiger?'

'What other side would I have in mind?'

'*Touché*.' He laughed softly. 'For a convent girl you ave a quick tongue.'

'You say terrible things to me, sir.'

'I suppose I do,' he agreed. 'You invite them, or perhaps I should say you incite them? You are running away from the meaning of life.'

'Why should you care?' Her eyes skimmed his face, but the firm brown features bore no traces of his thoughts; he could mask himself with Greek efficiency.

'Why?' A sombre look crept into his eyes. 'Because once before I saw a young life wasted, only there was no way to stop it from happening. I saw the light go out of a lovely pair of eyes and I tasted blood on the lips I kissed for the last time.'

His words sent a chill through Iris. 'I'm sorry—it was sad for you, and a great loss for Aleko.'

'You like my Aleko, *ne*?'

'Very much.'

'Even though he's like me?'

'He's a child——'

'And is therefore not a threat, eh?'

She remained silent, for to admit to Zonar that he was a threat was to admit it to herself. A little sigh of relief escaped her as Louise entered the room with her supper tray, unaware that the master of the house was there, standing close to the bed where Iris was huddled. Louise faltered just inside the room.

'Oh—I thought Miss was alone——' The girl gave him a questioning look.

'I brought in some witch-hazel.' He indicated the bottle, which he had placed on the bedside table. 'See to it that she applies it to her bruises; it should help to take away some of the sting.'

As he said this he glanced at Iris and for a moment an ironic smile glimmered in his eyes. 'Eat up your supper, Miss Ardath, and don't have a nightmare about cliff-hanging. Wipe it from your mind.'

'I'll try, sir.'

He glanced at his wristwatch. 'I must be off. I have some complimentary tickets for the new show at the Pavilion Theatre and I'm taking Miss Morel. I discovered in Paris that she enjoys a musical show.'

'Have a good evening, sir.'

'I intend to.' His eyes held hers. 'I'll put Aleko to bed and tell him not to disturb you any more tonight. *Adio.*'

As he passed Louise near the door he paused to take a look under the lids over the dishes on the tray. 'The lamb chops look delicious. See to it, Louise, that our patient eats every mouthful.' He was gone with a stride and the maid gave a rather nervous laugh as she gazed after him.

'I never get over how dark-looking he is,' she remarked as she closed the door. 'Fancy him thinking of the witch-hazel.'

'Yes ...' The look of bemusement lingered in Iris's eyes. 'He can be kind when he wants to be....'

CHAPTER SIX

YES, he was sometimes kind, but Iris's thoughts were dominated by the other side of Zonar Mavrakis, the man who had swept her into his arms and forced her to kiss him.

She couldn't imagine the same scene with Colette, who would yield her lips with eagerness and twine her arms closely around him, unafraid to meet his masculine demands.

'Will you eat your supper first, miss, before seeing to your bruises?'

Iris nodded and the tray was settled across her knees. 'I can manage to apply the witch-hazel,' she said. 'You run along and have your own supper, Louise.'

'But Mr Mavrakis said I was to help you, miss.'

'I shall manage all right,' Iris assured the girl. 'I expect you are longing to sit down after working about the house all day.'

'Kojak's on the telly—he's Greek as well.' Louise grinned. 'They are masterful, aren't they?'

'Oh yes.' Iris spoke drily. 'I expect they still regard women as goods and chattels; no doubt it's still part of their system to give a goat and some hens along with the bride.'

'Achille told cook that the *kyrios* lost his wife in an accident when the little boy was only a baby. I do think it's a shame, don't you, miss? Do you think he's keen on Miss Morel? She's very glamorous, isn't she? I jus don't know how she walks in those high heels, but I suppose being a model she's used to it.'

'Yes.' Iris reflected on her encounter with Colette in the garden; not so very long ago they had been schoolgirls together, now they were young women and involved in different ways with the same man. Fate, twisting itself into a strange knot.

'Go and enjoy your television programme, Louise,' she said. 'I'd better eat my chops before they get cold.'

'Right you are, miss. Don't forget about the witch-hazel or the *kyrios* will tick me off if he sees no improvement in those bruises of yours. My, but you did collect a crop of them, didn't you?'

'Yes.' Iris smiled wryly. 'Anyway, I don't intend to let Mr Mavrakis inspect them.'

'I don't suppose so, miss.' Louise giggled, 'but he knows how to get his own way, doesn't he? He's very dominating but in a way that isn't really bullying, if you know what I mean?'

'I know what you mean.' Iris shook salt on her potatoes and peas. 'He has a natural authority backed up by money and charisma.'

'Charisma, miss?'

'It's a Greek word meaning magnetism of a very personal kind. When some people enter a room you aren't immediately aware of them, but the *kyrios* makes himself felt.'

'Yes, that's exactly what he does, miss!' Louise looked impressed by Iris's explanation. 'Fancy you knowing that, coming from a convent and all ready to become a nun.'

Iris smiled at the girl's awestruck tone of voice. 'Even nuns know how many buns there are in a baker's dozen,' she said drily. 'They are often sent to work in some of the toughest areas of the world, and being a religious person doesn't mean being ignorant of the hard facts of life. Nuns are among the best nurses, you know.'

'Will you be a nurse, miss?'

'The Mother Superior will decide if I'm suited.'

Louise stood there studying Iris as she ate her supper and she was obviously mulling over in her mind the personal restrictions of a nun's life.

'It wouldn't be my cup of tea,' she remarked. 'I've a boy-friend and we'll get married when we've saved enough. I can't imagine not having someone special to care about me. It's such a nice feeling, miss, all warm and sort of exciting.'

'I daresay it is.' Iris smiled slightly.

'I couldn't give that up for anything, miss.' Louise backed to the door and opened it, as if suddenly she had to run away from Iris in case the urge to become a nun was catching. 'I'll say goodnight—don't forget the witch-hazel, will you?'

Iris's smile deepened as she shook her head. The door closed behind the girl and Iris pushed aside her dinner plate and glanced at her dessert, a pair of bell-shaped pears and cream to pour over them. Nice, the sort of dessert that would become a luxury when she left the villa and returned to the convent.

She ate the pears with leisurely enjoyment. Right now her employer would be dining with Colette before they drove to the theatre. Colette would be clad in a glamorous dress which she had probably bought in Paris. No doubt the two of them would discuss their meeting in Paris ... they would be at ease together, able to talk and laugh without any sense of conflict.

Perhaps they were on the verge of falling in love. I

felt warm and exciting, Louise had said, having someone who cared about you.

Iris set aside her tray and slid down against her pillows. She would never know the glamour of love, the excitement and the warmth, the dream merging into reality. She knew in which direction her destiny led ... it led away from the kind of dreams other girls were free to have.

It certainly led away from Zonar Mavrakis.

A hand climbed to the cross at her throat. 'The day will come when you will wrestle with a demon,' she had been warned by one of the Sisters, 'and you will need all your resistance to cast him out!'

Her fingers clung to the cross as if it could help her to hold back the tide of her forbidden thoughts. Because she had been taught to face the truth she knew that the tall Greek had forced his way past her defences ... when he spoke to her, when he looked at her, when he had touched her with his hands and lips she had felt as if her mind was dissolving from her body and she had wanted what he did to her, and he had known it. It was what tormented her most of all, knowing that his warm mouth on her skin had woken up all the repressed hunger for affection ... it was the first time she had ever been kissed and felt another human being so close to her. She had been so innocently unaware that the body was so sensitive and so eagerly responsive to the feel of a man.

Her face burned and even the fervent whisper of a few Hail Marys couldn't wipe out the memory of those moments when she had come so close to putting her arms around Zonar Mavrakis.

Had it been compassion for a man who had taken his son from the wrecked body of his wife?

Iris strove to believe it, but knew in her heart that she was fooling herself. She turned her face into the pillows and knew that the aching she felt inside her was unrelated to the battering her body had taken against the rough cliffside.

'I mustn't ... it's forbidden to feel like this!'

There against her closed eyelids she saw his face ... the compelling eyes, the bold Grecian nose, and most of all the dark mole low down on the left side of his jaw.

Iris clenched the bedcovers and knew that she was wrestling with her demon ... her awareness of her physical self, which she must deny if she was to find the total state of grace demanded of a nun. If she fled from the villa she couldn't run away from herself ... oh, what a fool she was to let this happen when she knew that she could never mean anything to him. He didn't take women seriously, least of all a plain young convent girl half his age, who had about as much sophistication as a garden moth.

'Fool ... you fool!' she berated herself. Wearily she climbed out of bed and reached for the bottle of witch-hazel. She applied it to her bruises, which looked shockingly black against the whiteness of her skin. She could feel a weak trembling at the back of her knees and her combination of aches brought tears to her eyes. It would have been a comfort to have someone caring for her right now, but she had grown up in an environment where pain was concealed or overcome. Self-indulgence of any sort was frowned upon at St Clare's.

Iris put on her nightdress and winced as she raised her arm to brush her hair. She studied her reflection in the mirror with self-critical eyes. Whatever had made Colette imagine that Zonar Mavrakis saw anything to attract him in the guileless-looking figure in the looking-glass? The long plain nightdress reached to her ankles and concealed what curves she had ... Colette had nothing to fear, and she like a fool was over-reacting because he had come to her rescue, plucking her off that cliff just as he would a kitten or a bird with a battered wing.

She climbed back into bed and settled down with a sigh. She was reaching out to switch off the lamp when the door opened and a sleepy-eyed Aleko poked his head around it.

'Can I come and sleep with you?' he asked.

Her first reaction was to refuse him, but even as she rose upon an elbow and was about to tell him to go back to his own room he came over and scrambled in beside her. He snuggled down close to her warmth. 'I had a bad dream,' he said. 'The one about the round-about.'

'Roundabout, Aleko?'

He blinked his black eyelashes and burrowed his head against her shoulder. 'It goes round and round and then I fall off.'

'I see. What did you have for supper?'

'Cheese omelette.'

'Do you reckon that had anything to do with your dream?'

'Probably.' He yawned widely and sniffed her skin. 'You smell antiseptic and you've got ever such a bruise on your arm.'

'It's witch-hazel you can smell—the bruises will go away. Do you often dream of the roundabout, Aleko?'

'Now and then.' His eyelids were growing weighted. 'It's nice here with you, Iris. You won't send me back to my own room, will you?'

She hesitated ... there was no harm in letting him

stay tonight, but it mustn't become a habit. She rather welcomed the company, and he was only a little boy, a young and innocent replica of the father. His eyes closed and his lips slackened as he drifted off to sleep, curled there against her in his blue pyjamas. Sometimes at the convent she had sat up with a sick infant, but letting one of them into bed hadn't been allowed. Never before had she shared her bed with anyone, hearing their breathing and feeling their movements as they slept. She put out the lamp and settled down to sleep herself.

She awoke with a start ... light was coming into her room from the gallery and someone was leaning over her bed. Bemused and still half asleep, she gazed up at the looming figure and saw his eyes glittering in the shadowy light.

'I wondered where the devil the boy was!' He growled the words. 'I looked in on him and his bed was empty. He's with you, eh?'

'Yes——' She lay there feeling threatened by the tall figure, uncertain if he was angry with her, or annoyed by his own alarm. 'He woke up from a dream he didn't like and came to me.'

'You being on hand, Miss Ardath, while I was out gallivanting, eh?'

'He doesn't often wake up once he goes to sleep,' she hedged, 'so it must have been a rather disturbing dream, sir.'

'He was no doubt disturbed by your own mishap.' He moved round the bed and took a look at his soundly sleeping son. 'If I lift him, he might wake and that would be a pity. He had better say with you until the morning.'

'I hope you don't mind?'

'Mind?' He raised an eyebrow. 'My son is a Mavrakis and is following a natural inclination, if you did but realise it.'

'He's just a little boy——'

'He's my son, *thespoinis.*' A glint came and went in the dark eyes. 'Also he misses what most other boys have, the affection and indulgence of a mother. Be careful he doesn't disturb you, you have enough bruises to contend with. By the morning you will feel as if you've been thrashed, so take things easy tomorrow. No outings with Aleko. Rest and recover.'

With that he left the room, closing the door quietly behind him and shutting her in the darkness. She lay there listening to Aleko's soft breathing and feeling the quick beating of her heart. There was a contradictory side to Zonar Mavrakis which was more troubling than his forceful ways ... he had a tenderness in him which revealed itself at unexpected moments, leaving a woman's defences in ruin around her.

He was a demon with diabolical charm, she told herself. She knew in her female bones that it had curiously pleased him to see her in bed with his child ... the son who would carry on his name and grow up in his tough and dominant image.

The next time Iris awoke the morning light was in the room. Louise had opened the curtains and there was a tea-tray on the bedside table. Aleko had departed, leaving the imprint of his head in the pillow, and as Iris sat up to pour a cup of tea she winced at the stiffness in her limbs. Her arms ached from the shoulder to the wrist and her hand trembled as she poured her tea.

Louise came back into the room carrying some fresh

bathroom towels. 'Morning, miss. How are you feeling?'

'As if I've been taken to pieces and put back together again.' Iris sipped her tea and wondered how she was going to make the effort to climb out of bed.

Louise gave her a sympathetic look. 'The little chap was waking up when I came in to open the curtains,' she said. 'These Greek children are very affectionate, aren't they? And then again he hasn't a mother to hug and kiss him, though I must say the *kyrios* is a very good father, busy man though he is. Do you reckon he's thinking of getting married again, miss? Achille drove him to the theatre with Miss Morel and they were talking a lot, and on the way home Achille said she had her head on his shoulder, and he went with her into the hotel and didn't come out again for nearly an hour.'

A nerve twisted inside Iris when Louise gave a knowing smile, as if to imply that he had gone with Colette to her suite and stayed to make love to her.

An image of him at her own bedside flashed across Iris's mind, jacket and tie discarded, silk shirt open at his muscular throat, a look of force and passion about him as he towered there in the semi-darkness and stared down at his son curled asleep at her side.

There had been a look in his eyes, an expansion of his pupils which had given him an emotional expression which was now explained. She explored her own feelings as she drank her tea ... was she shocked because Colette had been a convent pupil like herself, or did it offend her romantic belief that a man and woman should stand before an altar and have their love blessed by the sacrament of marriage?

She pushed aside the bedcovers and barely suppressed

a groan as she slid out of bed. She hobbled into the bathroom feeling as if she'd been beaten; Louise turned from the towel rack and gave her a look of concern. 'Perhaps you ought to see the doctor, miss?' she suggested. 'You could have put something out——'

'No.' Iris shook her head. 'I'll take a shower and that should help to loosen me up. I should have watched my step.'

'Are you sure you'll be all right, miss?' Louise hovered in the doorway.

'I'll be fine.' Iris managed to smile, though she felt weak in the knees and could barely raise her arm to turn on the shower. Once beneath the soothing warmth of the water she felt a little better and she lingered there, allowing the stream to wash down over her body. She massaged her arms and shoulders with her fingertips, but when she tried to bend, even her hips felt stiff.

'This,' she thought ironically, 'is how it feels to be old!'

Old ... the word drifted through her mind, life at its ebb and her years barren of romance.

'Don't be foolish,' she berated herself, stepping from the shower to wrap herself in one of the large warm towels. She patted herself dry and went into her bedroom ... pulling up short as she entered and saw the tall figure framed by one of the long windows. 'Oh ...' Her exclamation made him swing round to face her. His lean cheeks were shaven, his black hair was groomed, his suit was light beige with charcoal pinstripes over a charcoal shirt. He was ready to go to work, but he didn't move, he stood there frowning at her.

'I asked Louise how you were feeling,' he said at last. 'She told me you are stiff as a board.'

'I—I was,' Iris admitted, standing there large-eyed and wrapped in the towel, and still acutely aware that he had seen what it covered. 'I've showered and I feel easier——'

'Are you certain you haven't dislocated anything?' He came towards her and she instinctively backed away from him, locking the towel around her and defying him to lay a finger upon her ... no, not a single finger which had caressed Colette!

'I wouldn't be able to move at all, sir. The stiffness will go away.'

'You even sound stiff,' he drawled. 'And I do wish you'd stop looking at me as if I mean to rip that towel off you and have my way with your aching body. Do I strike you as such a monster, Miss Ardath?'

With an effort she pulled her gaze away from him. 'I think you realise, Mr Mavrakis, that I'm unused to seeing a man in my bedroom—it wasn't something they encouraged at St Clare's.'

'That's better,' his drawl deepened, 'now you sound less starchy. I am, however, going to insist that the doctor look you over and I've already telephoned him.'

'I wish you hadn't—I'm really quite all right,' she protested.

'You don't look it,' he said decisively, 'and I know damn well you aren't feeling it. As your employer I'm entitled to get you back into working order, am I not?'

'I can work, Mr Mavrakis. I haven't said that I'm too sick to take care of Aleko.' She had to tilt her head to look at him; standing there barefoot she barely came to his shoulder ... wide shoulders set on a straight spine, covered by the suit that was perfectly tailored to every bone and muscle of his big body, his collar and

:uffs of generous proportions suited to the width of his
vrists and his powerful neck.

That slightly raffish smile lifted the corner of his
ıpper lip. 'As caviar is packed tightly into a small jar,
ɔ has independence been packed into you. No, you
vouldn't complain, would you? A touch of the rack is
;ood for the soul, eh?'

Iris thought that one over and realised there was a
rain of truth in it; she had been brought up to endure
ather than complain, and there was no denying the
ıct that she did feel as if her body had been racked.

'I'd get back into bed,' he said. 'Is this your night-
ress?'

Louise had laid out a fresh one for her, long and
lain and high at the neck. He picked it up and gave
 a look that spoke volumes. Iris gave him a shocked
ɔok, which he imitated as he handed her the garment.
'll turn my back, miss. I wasn't going to send you up
ı flames by suggesting I help you on with that mid-
'ictorian nightgown.'

'I should hope not!' Iris clutched hold of it and
'ent into the bathroom to put it on. Her cheeks were
ushed and the weakness in her legs seemed worse than
ver. He really was the limit, coming and going in her
ɔom as if he had the right to do so ... it was all very
'ell for him to talk teasingly about being old enough
› be her father, but to the other people in this house
e was a man and she was a woman and before long
ıey'd be saying about her what they were saying about
olette.

'Are you respectable?' His arms swung her off her
:et and carried her with ease to her bed. 'How fragile
ɔu feel, Miss Ardath. I believe you clung to those cliffs
y will alone.'

'My arms wouldn't agree with you——' She bit her lip and turned her gaze from the bold line of his profile.

'What the devil does a man do with the likes of you?' His breath raked warm across her face. 'Do you suffer everything in silence—everything?'

'I don't like fuss and bother——'

'Emotions, as I've told you before, young woman are meant to be used, not repressed.' He lowered he to the bed and was about to adjust the covers aroun her when he caught sight of her feet, black and blu against the whiteness of the sheets. He drew in hi breath audibly and reached for her right foot, whicl he cradled in his big hand. Iris gazed from her foo to his face in a kind of helplessness.

'The bruising looks worse than it is,' she said. 'I'v the kind of skin that shows every knock.'

'So I see.' He moved his thumb against her instep 'You need to spend time in the sunshine of Greece, t run wild in the sage and the cistus; to bathe in the se and relax on the sands. You would soon develop a tan

'There's no point in talking about it.' Her voice ha faded to a husky whisper. 'Please stop talking abou things I can't have.'

'You can have it!' His black brows were drawn to gether in thought. 'You can fly to Greece wit Aleko——'

'I can't!' she wriggled her foot until his grip tigh ened. 'You know it isn't possible, *kyrie*.'

'Do I?' His eyes brooded upon her. 'Perhaps so— must remain here a while longer and there is alway the chance that you would find a Greek cliff to fall ove What is it, I wonder—what curse brings trouble to m door just when I——?'

He broke off and gently inserted her bruised feet in he bedcovers, then he wandered away and stood frown-ng out of the window at the sun gleaming on the nglish sea. Iris gazed at him uncertainly and won-lered what he meant by his broken words ... though sophisticated man in many ways, he was foremost a reek and the superstitions of his people were in his eins.

Iris drew her feet together and still his touch lin-ered warm against her skin, probably impressed there ecause her skin was sore. Did he believe that the un-imely death of his young wife had left a cloud hanging ver any other love he might seek? Did he feel some ind of a foreboding as he stood there, thinking per-aps that Colette could be hurt by her association with im?

There was a knock upon the bedroom door and onar swung round. The door opened to admit Louise ollowed by a moustached man carrying a black case.

'Dr Warren is here, sir.' Louise slid her gaze from onar to Iris.

'Good morning.' The two men shook hands. 'Miss rdath, my son's governess, has some rather severe ruising from a fall and I would appreciate it, Dr Varren, if you would look her over and prescribe some-hing for her pain.'

'I heard something about this—may I?' Dr Warren at down in a chair beside the bed and his eyes were ntent upon Iris's face as he took her left wrist in his ngers. She knew her pulse was beating rapidly from combination of nerves and the presence of Zonar at he foot of her bed. After checking her heart rate the octor glanced at her employer. 'I should like to ex-mine Miss Ardath.'

'By all means.' Zonar withdrew from the room and closed the door. Dr Warren gave Iris a considering look.

'Have you any specific pain?' he asked.

She shook her head. 'It's an all-over kind of ache,' she admitted. 'My arms feel rather wrenched——'

'Let's have a look at you.'

The examination was thorough and took about twenty minutes, and at the end of it Dr Warren folded his stethoscope and pursed his lips. 'You are badly bruised, young woman, and your system has undergone something of a shock. I'm going to prescribe a tonic as well as medication for your aches and pains. I suppose your eyesight is all right?'

'Why—yes.' She looked at him bewilderingly.

He smiled slightly. 'When young women fall over cliffs I am inclined to wonder why, and you have the kind of wide blue eyes which are sometimes myopic. Weren't you looking where you were going—or were you running from someone?'

'Someone?' She drew back against her pillows almost defensively.

The doctor glanced over towards the closed door, then ran his gaze over her again. 'Mr Mavrakis is Greek, isn't he? He's a stranger to this district—the new owner of the big hotel, the Monarch, I understand?'

'Yes.' Iris watched as the doctor scribbled a prescription for her. 'I hope you don't think Mr Mavrakis had anything to do with my fall? I was just barely holding on and he climbed down to get me.'

'The knight to the rescue, eh?' Dr Warren studied what he had written as if he had trouble understanding his own writing. 'Do you like working for him, young woman? You seemed nervous of him, do you

:now that? After he left the room your pulse rate teadied down.'

'I was rather agitated because he sent for you, doctor. t wasn't altogether an untruth. 'It isn't as if I'm sick. feel all right apart from the bruising.'

'All the same,' the doctor rose to his feet, 'I'm going o suggest to Mr Mavrakis that you remain in bed for a ouple of days. No arguments, young woman. You've ıad something of a shock, and I will add that I don't are for the way you girls go on diets these days. It isn't ıecessary in your case.'

'I—I don't diet,' she exclaimed.

'You're a trifle underfed,' he said quizzically. 'You ıren't a Devonshire girl, are you? Do you come from ,ondon?'

'No, from Essex.' Her fingers linked themselves to- ether and she found herself trying to avoid Dr Varren's shrewd gaze. 'I live in a convent there and his job is a kind of sabbatical for me. I'm to become a ıun.'

'Ah!' The locks of his medical-case snapped together. So that's it, eh?'

She looked at him then, enquiringly, but whatever ıe had in mind he chose to leave there.

'Take care of yourself, Miss Ardath, and try to avoid umbling over any more of our Devonshire cliffs. I'll peak with your employer and arrange about your nedication.'

'Thank you, doctor.' She watched as the door closed ehind him and very gradually her fingers relaxed heir hold upon each other. She sighed, nestled her ead against the pillow and closed her eyes. Suddenly ll she wanted was to go off to sleep and not have to hink about anything. Slowly she relaxed and pushed out of her mind a sense of guilt at lazing in bed in the day time. At the convent she rose at six in the morning and each hour of the day was filled with activity. Through her lashes she gazed at the sunlight through the long arching windows; a scent of the seashore drifted in and she caught the purring sound of a motor boat on the water. The gulls mewed and she pictured them flying around the immense rock that stood offshore deep in the water, speckled and graceful with the sunlight on their wings.

She slept and time stood still, a dreamless gulf of warmth in which she lay cradled, her lashes quivering just a fraction on her cheeks as if momentarily she felt the long shadow that fell across her bed, and then silently withdrew.

During the next few days Iris rested a good deal. The doctor came again to see her, declared her much better and permitted her to get up and about. The first thing she and Aleko did was to go down on the beach ... ah, but it felt good to breathe the sea air and feel the warm sun on her skin. It felt good to be alive!

The days merged into evenings when business associates of Zonar's came to dine at the villa, filling the *salon* with their talk and a haze of cigar smoke.

Iris would listen to them and it would all feel so strangely different from life as she had known it at St Clare's, where the evenings were passed so quietly except for the chiming of bells and the rustling of the habit as the nuns made their way to evening prayer in the chapel.

Quite often Colette came up to the villa. She would look decorative while the men played pool in the long cool billiard room. Sometimes she would sing at the

lossy black piano; Iris remembered that she had taken
essons while at the convent and though her voice
'asn't all that vibrant it had a husky sensuality which
eemed to please Zonar. *'C'est l'heur de bien faire?'*
Colette would murmur, looking into his dark eyes, and
vith a smile he would hand her a glass of champagne.

Iris would sit half-hidden, in a corner, and not really
aind that he ignored her presence. She preferred
nonymity. While Colette had all his attention she
idn't bother Iris with questions and curiosity. She
asked in Zonar's smile and flirted openly with him in
ont of his other guests; she emitted the excitement of
woman who had a man interested in her, sun-tanned
aoulders rising from the *décolleté du jour* of a Parisian
vening dress, a golden chain glinting around her
aroat

When she and Iris did find themselves alone she
idn't hesitate to let it be known that her objective was
aarriage into the Mavrakis family.

'With Greeks a girl has to be rather careful,' she said.
Even in this day and age they want to be a girl's first
aan.'

'Will that be the case?' Iris couldn't resist asking. She
'as always a little cool these days with her one-time
iend, and she always made sure they didn't converse
a the vicinity of the cliffs.

'Of course, *chérie*.' Colette laughed and leaned for-
'ard to pour another cup of coffee from the silver pot.
seemed to Iris that Colette's laugh was a little off-key.
Zonar was telling me the other day that the Greeks
ave a saying. "To love is nothing. To be loved is
omething. To love and be loved is everything." You
ouldn't take him for a man in the least sentimental,
ould you?'

'People can be deceptive,' Iris murmured, looking cool and collected in a simple cream skirt with a cognac-coloured shirt. Colette had been up to the stables to ride; she had flung off a jaunty suede hat and a checked riding-coat; her model's figure was flattered by a suede waistcoat, pale beige breeches tucked into suede knee-boots. She looked, Iris thought, as if she had stepped from the cover of *Country Life* magazine; a girl for all occasions, the ideal companion for a successful man.

'Are you deceptive, *chérie*?' Colette leaned back against the wine leather of a club couch, booted legs crossed as she sipped her coffee. Her eyes, feathered with colour even though she had been out riding, dwelt on Iris with a faint amusement. 'I wonder what lurks deep in your soul? Is there any passion there, I wonder? Still waters run deep, so it is said.'

'Did you have a good ride?' Iris evaded the question. 'They provide good horses at Honeyton, don't they? One of the girls told me they are moorland bred. Aleko loves them.'

'You should learn to ride.' Colette nibbled a biscuit. 'Are you scared of big muscular creatures—like men and horses?'

'No, I'm not scared.' Iris's smile was a shade wistful though she didn't realise it. 'I suppose I don't want to get a taste for pleasures I can't enjoy in the future.'

'Still set on self-sacrifice, eh? Colette pressed flame-tipped fingers to a delicate yawn. 'How you can face the prospect of it is a mystery to me—I mean, after all this!'

Iris glanced around the room, with its maize-gold carpet, its tastefully arranged paintings and figurines, its ivory-silk curtains tied back with sashes. A Regency room, elegant and warm-coloured, with sunlight spilling in from outside and the sing-song of birds.

'It is a charming room,' Iris admitted.

'Zonar has a house in Greece.' Colette studied her fingernails. 'I'm longing to see it, and that island his brother owns. Petaloudes, island of butterflies!'

'Which fly blind and are guided by scent alone.' Zonar had said that love was blind; perhaps he chose not to see that Colette's charming façade concealed a desire for the pleasures and treasures which money could buy. Once he had loved with his heart ... perhaps this time he was content to love with his senses. Colette would know how to satisfy those, and Aleko seemed to find her amusing; he referred to her as Pussy Cat because of her slanting eyes. The other day he had asked her if she could purr; she had patted him on the head, called him her *petit* and looked speculative, as if already she had decided that he could go away to school when the time came and not get underfoot.

With those slanting eyes Colette was gazing at a painting on a nearby wall; it seemed of the French school, of a girl neck-deep in harebells.

'She reminds me of you!' Colette exclaimed. 'You are rather fey, are you not, *chérie*?'

'Not quite of this world, eh?' The terrace windows darkened as a tall figure came and stood there, blotting out the sunlight. Iris cast a startled glance in that direction and saw Zonar looking big and easy in a sweater and slacks; his sweater had Greek designs knitted into it, the dark cashmere close against his throat.

'*Mon ami.*' Colette held out a hand to him and he strolled across to where she sat, took her fingers in his and briefly kissed them. 'You are very much of this world,' he said to her.

'And glad of it!' Her eyes went up and down his large frame. 'You do look nice, Zonar! I haven't seen that sweater before; how well it suits you!'

'It was knitted for me by hand and I received it in the post this morning.'

'Really? And who knits you such attractive sweaters, eh? If it is a pretty woman, then I will scratch out her eyes.'

'Lay one finger on Fenella and you will answer to me, *petite* cat.' He glanced at the coffee pot. 'A cup of coffee would be welcome. I took my son down to the hotel this morning and he has been in and out of everything; I have left him with a boy who is staying there with his parents, so I'd be obliged, Miss Ardath, if you'll collect him some time this afternoon.'

'Of course, sir.' Iris poured coffee for him and held out the cup and saucer. When he took it she rose to her feet and excused herself. 'I have a few chores to attend to,' she murmured.

'Do you like my sweater?' he asked.

'It's beautifully knitted, sir.' Suddenly an idea struck her and she met his eyes. 'Is it your birthday, by any chance?'

A smile tweaked his lip and he inclined his head.

'Many happy returns——' but before she could finish Colette jumped to her feet and flung her arms around his neck, bringing his head down to her so she could press her lips to his.

'You should have told me, darling! When we go into town I will buy you something very, very nice.' She stroked a hand down his jaw, and with a little shrug Iris turned away and quietly left the room. She glanced at the hall clock and saw that it was close on lunch-time; suddenly she didn't want to sit at lunch with Colette and watch her flirting with Zonar. She would collect some sandwiches and a flask of tea from the kitchen and go down to Peachstone Cove for a solitary picnic lunch; the beach was so named because the pale sands were scattered with reddish stones, round enough to roll.

Iris made ham sandwiches for herself and a pot of tea which she could pour into a flask. She was chatting to Cook when Achille came in from the garage, where he'd been waxing the cars. He grinned when he saw Iris and as he rinsed his hands at the sink he looked her up and down.

'Where are you off to?' he asked, his black hair raking his forehead as he stood wiping his hands, his shirt wide open across his brawny chest.

'I'm going for a walk,' she replied in her coolest voice, holding the flask steady as she poured the tea into it.

'Alone?' he quizzed her. 'You won't find that very entertaining, so why not invite me along?'

'I have to fetch Aleko from the hotel quite soon.' She picked up her package of sandwiches and smiled at Cook. 'Thank you for the ham; it looks delicious.'

'So do you,' Achille drawled. 'Like one of those water-ices that melt on the tongue.'

Iris ignored him and walked out of the kitchen, hastening her footsteps across the courtyard in case he took it into his head to follow her. She avoided the man whenever possible; he didn't bother her when she had Aleko with her, well aware that the boy told his father everything that went on, but seeing her today with a picnic lunch he had probably guessed that she was going to the beach alone.

She paused and glanced back at the house. It looked quiet and slumbrous there in the sunlight; perhaps she should eat her sandwiches in the gazebo and avoid the beach, which was very little used by comparison to the wider, more sandy beaches near to town. This end of Tormont was more rugged and lonely.

Glimpses of the sea sparkled in the sunlight ... the sun itself seemed to smoulder in its own radiance, up there in that Gauguin-blue sky. Across the bay the view was crystalline, and a sweet warm breath of wind came and went against her skin and moved the spidery fronds of the tamarisk trees. A sea bird stretched its wings and seemed to hang in stillness for several seconds against the gold and blue, then it swooped down towards the sands, and Iris followed the path that led downwards.

She needed to be alone; she was far away from the quiet chapel of St Clare's where she had sometimes sat with her thoughts when they troubled her.

Had she felt troubled before or after Zonar had entered the villa wearing the Greek-patterned sweater? She wasn't sure, and yet had the feeling that her sense of disquiet was connected with that faraway person named Fenella. When he spoke her name his eyes had looked ... loving?

Yes, Iris told herself. Zonar cared for Fenella in a way that he didn't care for Colette ... it was as if he allowed Colette to charm him even as his heart stayed uninvolved.

She walked out of the sunlight into the shadows made by the trees arching over the steep pathway to the beach, rambling downwards in steps bounded by thick clumps of ferns and bushes. There was a drone of insects in the stillness, trailing boughs to be avoided, and caught in some shrub the corpse of a seagull, somehow reminding Iris of her mishap on the cliffs. Her bruises had faded but the memory lingered, drifting into her dreams at night and waking her up in alarm ... it was as if she was falling again, but no one bothered this time to stretch out a hand to stop her from plunging into the cold sea.

She heard the sea as she reached the cove, shaped like a moon cut in half and scattered with the red globular stones. It was lonely here, just a little sinister, the cove enclosed by great boulders that pushed up out of the water like the snouts of sea monsters.

Iris pushed out of her mind the disquiet she felt. She found a patch of smooth sand and laid her rug down on it. Gulls flew in over the cliffs with their greedy swoops and cries and the waves struck upwards and broke on the rocks in spates of sparkling water. Iris breathed a sigh as she sat there alone and let the sounds stroke away her feeling of pensiveness.

'Have a sandwich and a cup of tea,' she told herself, and proceeded to do so. The ham was thick and delicious and she chewed it appreciatively; the tea was hot and sweet, and after enjoying her lunch she lay back on the rug, kicked off her sandals and decided to take a short nap. Aleko would be enjoying himself with a playmate of his own age, so she wouldn't fetch him just yet.

She closed her eyes and listened to the sea ... she had a feeling almost of being cradled, but wouldn't allow her thoughts to venture into the deeper, more secret realms of her mind. She didn't dare to risk a confrontation with what lay in hiding there; it had to be walled up until it stopped crying for its release. Starved of light and nourishment it would cease to be ... it had to be that way.

She woke abruptly, then sat up with a startled gasp. Time had slipped away and she was surrounded by the fading gold of late afternoon, the lengthening shadows, and a quiver of red on the water. Oh lord, she was supposed to collect Aleko from the hotel and here she was, still down in the cove where the sea had come well in among the rocks. She scrambled to her feet and searched for her sandals.

'Looking for these?'

A figure stepped from the shadows and stood darkly against the abundance of burning sky. Her sandals dangled by the straps from his fingers.

'You!'

'Yes, governess, me.' He came towards her with an air of deliberation; she reached out a hand for her sandals, but he withheld them and she saw his teeth as he smiled.

'I'd have joined you a little sooner, but I had to drive to the station with the boss so he could meet some VIPs, who then had tea at the hotel which held me up a little longer. The kid was there, so I guessed you were still here.'

Iris wetted her lips which had gone curiously dry. 'I—I'll have my sandals, if you don't mind?' She held out a hand but wouldn't take a step that would bring her nearer to Achille, whose muscular frame against the red sea and sky filled her with a dreadful feeling of threat. Her heart hammered, and she couldn't see a way of getting past him to the cliff steps. If she ran he'd grab at her with those thick hands and pull her into those arms that were dark with hair.

His answer was to drop the sandals near his own feet, pressed into the sand which his legs straddled. 'If you want them so badly, governess, come and get them.'

The only thing Iris wanted badly was to get to those steps and home to the villa, but Achille was barring her way, and in the other direction was the looming rocks and the splashing waves.

'The tide is coming in,' she said. 'You can see that for yourself——'

'I give it another half hour, which gives me plenty of time for what I want—you know what I want, don't you, sweetheart?'

'Yes, you want to lose a well-paid job, don't you, Achille?' She strove to keep the panic out of her voice but could feel it growing inside her; each moment the cove was darkening and she didn't know what she'd do if Achille leapt at her. She felt defenceless ... angry and afraid.

'You won't tell anyone. You're the sort who keeps things to yourself, aren't you?' He began to close in on her, his hands tensile and ready at the sides of his trousers. 'Come, there's more fun in it, governess, if you don't fight a man. Girls are always a bit nervy at first, but they go really crazy once they've had a taste of a man. You'll see. You and I will be very good friends afterwards, then when we've a bit of spare time we can often get together. Come on, don't back away from me or you'll make me lose my temper, and I wouldn't want that nice soft skin of yours to get bruised again.'

With a sudden lunge he flung out his long arms and almost had hold of her, but she leapt to one side and had access to the cliff steps if she could reach them. He was much heavier than she was and Iris knew she could outrun him if she could elude him. She started to run and then cried out as one of his powerful hands closed on her shirt; it began to rip away but held where the line of buttons were, and her scream ripped as she felt the savage enclosure of his arm around her body.

He yanked her to him, almost crushing the breath

from her lungs. Fear and repulsion raked across her mind as his mouth searched openly for hers; she snapped her head aside and felt the self-inflicted pain up the side of her neck.

'You'll kiss me,' he panted. 'I'll warm you up, you little madam, going about that house all prim and cool and looking as if you keep your feelings in the fridge. I know your sort! Hot as mustard when you really get stirred up!'

Iris felt as if her spine would crack as Achille exerted his strength and arched her body across his arm, putting his lips where her shirt was torn open. His mouth was hot, seeking, and then she couldn't keep her balance any more and felt him bearing her to the sands. He was on top of her and it was like a nightmare she couldn't escape from; holding her secure, he ripped her shirt right open and fumbled at the waistband of her skirt.

She fought and struggled but was pinned down by his weight; she felt him tear open the zip of her skirt and push at the material until he loosened it from around her waist and hips. She could hear the rasp of his breath and smell the tobacco he smoked, then shockingly she felt cool air on her legs and the hard heat of his hand stroking her.

'Ahh, what legs you have, *pedhaki mou*, so smooth and slim ... by hell, will you be still!'

She cried a name, but wasn't certain she cried it aloud until Achille taunted her. 'He won't come and help you this time, governess. He's too wrapped up in his own affairs, so forget him and be still!'

His hand gripped her thigh and, tormentedly, she thrust her knee upwards. Achille grunted as her knee drove into him and when she felt a slackening of his grip she strove to roll free of him.

'No, you don't!' Even as she found her feet his hand grasped her right ankle and he toppled her on to her face ... pain exploded in her head, for as she hit the sand her forehead struck against one of the larger stones that littered the beach, hard and smooth as marble. Consciousness slipped from her and everything went dark as she lay there slack as a doll, with Achille leaning over her.

CHAPTER SEVEN

It was the cold slap of water that revived Iris. It had washed in through the groins of rock and crept up the beach until it found her where she lay.

Her head was throbbing and she could feel the water lapping around her feet and legs ... she slowly sat up, shivering as the cold air threaded its way through the rents in her shirt. She glanced around her and saw the looming rocks and the pale glimmer of starlight on the sea, cresting the waves as they came riding into the cove.

'Oh God!' She put a hand to her forehead and felt a stickiness there and the soreness of broken skin. Reeling, she stood up and took several deep breaths of air in order to steady herself; she remembered what had happened before she had struck her head and passed out, but she didn't want to think of what could have taken place while she had lain unaware. The waves rolled in and the water climbed up past her ankles and she knew she had to make the effort to climb the cliff steps before the cove was flooded. All those steps and then the garden to traverse, hoping against hope that no one would see her in this bedraggled state and start to ask questions ... least of all her employer.

She shied away from the very thought of him seeing her like this, the front of her shirt torn open, her skirt wet with sea water, her forehead skinned and bruised from her fall. He'd demand to know what had happened to her and she would have to lie. She couldn't possibly tell him that his chauffeur had assaulted her putting into words the ugliness of it, and seeing the storm gathering in his eyes. She knew he'd beat hell out of Achille and she couldn't face any more violence.

Still feeling groggy, she sloshed through the water to the steps and started the long climb to the villa garden. It was dark and the steps were rough beneath her bare feet; unseen creatures rustled in the bushes, and she couldn't rid herself of the image of someone leaping out on her again.

She was stumbling and wearied by the time she reached the clifftop, and she could feel her forehead bleeding again. Holy Mother, let her reach the villa and get safely to her room without being seen! Crossing the hall from the side door was nerve-racking, and her heart was in her throat when she caught the sound of voices and laughter coming from the *salon*. She forced her tired legs up the stairs and along the gallery, and breathed a sigh of thankfulness upon reaching her own door. Almost faint with relief, she shut herself safely inside and sank down in a chair to recover her breath.

Thank God there were guests for the evening to keep Conar occupied ... she couldn't have borne it had he seen her creeping back into the house in this state.

She must get these torn things off! She must shower and tidy herself up and then if he sent someone to fetch her ... there in the bathroom with the door bolted she stared at herself in the mirror and saw the look of disbelief in her own eyes. She looked like a rag doll which had been dropped into a muddy puddle and dragged out again!

With hands that shook she discarded her torn and muddied clothes and stepped under the shower, turning the nozzle full force so that water pounded her skin and gradually washed away from her body the feeling of having been manhandled.

She soaped herself all over and used the loofah until she stung with cleanliness, but she couldn't reach into her mind and scrub away the memory of her struggle with Achille. The marks of his fingers were on her arms, and there were more marks against the whiteness of her thigh. She was unsure about the extent of the assault on her, she knew only that she had lain unconscious long enough for Achille to have achieved his purpose, and it was that heated look of purpose in his eyes which she remembered most of all as she stepped from under the shower and dried herself.

The wall mirror gave back her reflection ... she looked unaltered except for the remnants of terror in her eyes, and the abrasion on her forehead which she must try and hide with her hair. She picked up her torn shirt and her slip with the broken strap; she told herself ruefully that if she went on like this she would soon be very low on shirts, and this nice silk one had been one of those which Zonar had bought her. It was beyond repair ... just as her own innocence seemed to be.

What ought she to do? Leave the villa and go back to the convent? Her fingers slowly clenched the ruined shirt into a ball of silk, which she took into the bedroom and concealed in her handbag. She'd dispose of it in the morning, like evidence of guilt, as if what had happened down in the cove had been with her consent. Achille would swear so, and because she had crept back into the house without telling anyone it would look as if he told the truth.

Sighing, she went to the dressing-table and began to brush her hair, smoothing it across her forehead so it concealed the evidence of her fall. She couldn't bear to think of Zonar ever knowing about that degrading struggle on the sand, the touch of another man's hands on her body, the hot feel of lips that snarled at her in the dark, the awful helplessness of it all.

They called it lust ... in love itself there had to be an element of lust, and with a little cry she turned from the mirror and buried her face in her hands.

She didn't hear a knock on her bedroom door; she wasn't aware of someone entering her room until a hand touched her shoulder, lightly enough and yet it went through her like an electric shock. She quivered and drew quickly away from him, dropping her hands from her face.

'Where the devil have you been?' he demanded. 'Not a soul has seen you for hours, and I brought Aleko back with me from the hotel. What's the matter with you, eh?'

He turned her around to face him and she had to fight to compose her features.

'I—I went for a bus ride.' Iris had never lied so blatantly in her life before. 'It went further than I thought and I—I lost myself at a place where there were a lot of boats. I knew Aleko would be all right if he was at the hotel, so I had some tea and then managed to get the correct bus back to Tormont. It was dark by then. I could hear you had people in the *salon*, so I came straight upstairs and took a shower.'

Zonar had listened intently to what she told him, and she had to control an urge to cover her forehead with her hand in case he noticed the contusion. She was searching her mind wildly for an explanation should his keen eyes notice it just under her hair.

'You look—odd.' His eyes narrowed as they raked

over her face and down her neck to where her robe was sashed in place. 'Has something frightened you?'

'No.' She forced her lips into a smile. 'Why should I be frightened?'

'I don't know, but there's a look in your eyes I can't quite fathom, and it isn't like you to go off alone when I've given you an order connected with Aleko. Have you been telling me the truth?'

The glitter of his eyes filled her with a quick fear of being discovered and again she lied to him. 'Of course. I got on the wrong bus and it took me miles out of the way. I'm sorry about it. It won't happen again—in fact——'

'In fact?' he took her up.

'I've been thinking of giving you my notice. I think I ought to go back to St Clare's. I don't really belong here——'

'I shall tell you when you can go, and it isn't yet!' His hands closed hard upon her shoulders, a grip that she felt to her bones, but not in the repulsed way she had felt when Achille laid his hands on her. Everything seemed to quicken inside her, and then it was just as well he was holding her because her knees almost buckled beneath her.

'You feel as weak as water.' He stared down at her face, searching it with dark eyes. 'Is that what you've been doing all the afternoon, going round in circles trying to convince yourself that you should run away from me?'

'From you?' She stared up at him, knowing what her senses wanted and what she must deny herself.

'Yes! You know as well as I do that a man and a girl can't live under the same roof and not be aware of each other——'

'You have Colette,' she broke in. 'Please let me go way—just let me go!'

'I'm well aware that I could have Colette, or any one f a dozen others like her. But you—you are strange, eserved, intriguing. I'm not allowing you to go back that house of dry bones and good deeds, to wrap ourself in nun's weeds and deny yourself this,' his lips ressed her eyes, 'and this,' his lips took hers and his rong arms lifted her from the floor so she was held ompletely by him. Until now she hadn't known that eaven could be found on earth, but here it was, and e could hear herself sighing little sighs and moving erself in pleasure against his muscularity.

His searching lips pushed open her robe and their uch against her bare skin was a pleasure almost beond bearing. 'Zonar!' She gasped his name, saying it oud for the first time and hearing herself say it with sudden realisation of shock.

'No!' She pushed away from him and taken by surrise he dropped her to her feet. She backed away from m, pulling together the edges of her robe. Her legs ere shaking beneath her and she felt as if the room as tilting under her feet. Nightmare and dream came gether in her confused mind and it was as if she was own in the cove again, knowing only that she was reatened.

'Haven't you done enough to me?' she gasped. ou're a brute—a beast—all I want is to be left alone! ll you want is to destroy me!'

He stood there, his face a mask in which the eyes one were alive, seething as if with flame.

'Is that what you truly believe?' he demanded. 'Or is what you want to believe?'

She held the collar of her robe against her throat and

the man in front of her swam into focus again out o
the welter of confusion which had swept through he
mind as the sea had swept in dark swirls in and out o
the rocky groins.

Zonar, she realised. His the arms, the lips, the warn
hardness she had wanted to melt into.

'Well?' he almost shouted. 'Do you think I'm out t
destroy your puritanical little dream of being a nun
Do you?'

'Yes,' she said.

'Yes, yes,' he agreed, almost with a snarl. 'I'd like t
rip right out of your mind the very idea of sterility–
in fact I'm tempted to throw you on that bed and prov
conclusively what you were made for.' He took a ste
forward, then swung away from her, mouthing an oat
in Greek.

'By the gods, you almost drive me to it! Get yoursel
dressed and come downstairs to the *salon*. My brothe
and his wife are here from Greece and I want you t
meet them.'

Surprise jabbed at her, and then she recalled wha
Achille had said about taking Zonar to the station t
meet some VIPs. Lion Mavrakis and his wife Fenell
the only woman who could make Zonar look tender.

'Please, not tonight?' she pleaded.

'Tonight,' he said firmly. 'My brother and his wif
are in Devon for only a few days, then Fenny goes int
hospital for a minor operation and Lion will want t
be with her. There seems some chance that they ma
have a child—strangely enough Lion is not as co
cerned for this to happen as Fenny is. She lost thei
first child; I was with her and I know how hard sh
took it. She's a sweet person, so you will come down t
dinner and meet her.'

'It's an order, sir?' Iris asked quietly.

'An order,' he agreed. 'You owe me a little obedience fter this afternoon, wouldn't you agree?'

A shiver of recollection ran through her; he must ave noticed for he frowned. 'Where were you, Iris?'

'I told you——'

'You rambled on about something, but I think you 'ere inventing every word.' His dark eyes narrowed ntil there was just a glitter at the back of his lashes. Vere you with a man? I'd be inclined to think it of ny girl but you, and I think I might break his eck——'

'You're talking nonsense,' she broke in.

'Really?' He raised an eyebrow. 'You're talking to our employer.'

'Sometimes you behave more like a dictator!'

'Do I?' A smile moved in and out of his eyes. 'If you iink I'm a bit of a tyrant, just wait until you meet ion. I believe Fenny alone has the key to his heart, id the poor girl had to go to hell and back in order to t it. Do I seem hard to you, *thespoinis*?'

Hard, tough, indomitable. She could only incline r head ... perhaps all Greeks were that way until a oman found the key that unlocked the heart of them. iddenly she felt curious and wanted to see the English rl about whom he spoke with such tender feeling, 'en a kind of intimacy; he had been with her, he said, hen she had lost her baby. He implied that life had ot always been smooth sailing for her with the power-l head of the Mavrakis Corporation.

'All right,' Iris murmured. 'I'll get ready.'

'I'm going to choose your dress.' He strode to the oset and flung open the doors and Iris watched as he gered the dresses ... she felt a tingling sensation to the bottom of her spine, as if he ran his hands dow over her and felt the fabric of her being. He took on of the dresses from the rail, crêpe-de-chine in a sof shade of cream.

'A very good choice in my estimation.' He laid i across the bed and his eyes held a gleam of arrogance 'I shall expect you downstairs in about half an hour I'm allowing Aleko to dine with us as this is a specia occasion and he's chattering away to Fenny right now Can you manage on your own?'

'I've been managing to dress myself since I was a lo younger than Aleko,' she rejoined.

'In convent clothing,' he allowed. 'That evenin dress has a zip from the nape of the neck to the derrièr and you might need assistance with it.'

His eyes held hers, then with a slight laugh h strolled to the door, big and assured in a wine-coloure evening jacket over dark trousers, a dark bow tie against his white shirtfront. 'I'm being fatherly,' h mocked. 'I'm well aware that your sense of propriet wouldn't permit you to be helped into the dress—as help my Aleko when he puts his jersey on back t front.'

'I am a little older than Aleko,' she said drily. 'An I do assure you, sir, that I shan't join your dinner part wearing the dress back to front.'

'Funny girl.' He stood holding the door ajar. 'Secre tive as well, when you want to be, but I warn you I sha find out where you went and what you did all afte noon.'

Her heart gave an erratic beat; her feelings were sti raw from that encounter on the beach, but she didn think it showed outwardly that she had been ma treated by his driver. No, she assured herself, he wa eing inquisitive because she was usually so obedient vhen it came to taking orders.

'I have this feeling you're hiding something from me.' Iis gaze flicked over her, then he glanced at his wrist-vatch. 'I'm timing you, so don't take all night getting ressed.'

He was gone with the words, in that decisive way of is, and Iris stood there and still seemed to see the tall ark image of him, one of those satanic brows half aised in a mixture of mockery and threat. She had to ress and go downstairs because he demanded it, but t the same time she felt curious about Fenella Mav-akis and wished to see what she was like . . . this woman onar had no right to want because she was his rother's wife.

In less than half an hour Iris was dressed; she'd had little trouble with her long concealed zip at the back f the evening dress he'd chosen for her, but now it was n and it fitted her nicely, falling in delicate grace to er ankles and draped softly around her shoulders so er neck was bare, revealing the little gold cross she lways wore. Her delicately strapped evening shoes had vo inch heels, so she walked back and forth across her edroom a few times in order to accustom herself to the el of them.

She had to admit that she looked a totally different rl from the one who had first arrived here in a badly ting blouse and skirt, wearing those shoes Zonar had disliked. She stretched a leg and somewhat guiltily lmired the slenderness of her leg in sheer tights; the oes Zonar had bought her seemed to emphasis the ie bones of her ankles. This was vanity, but she uldn't help but like the feel of silk against her skin . her hand stretched out to lift a scent bottle and

apply its fragrance; the next moment Iris was hasten
ing from the room as if from the devil's whisper.

She felt the sudden grip of shyness when she neare
the salon; she nervously stroked the skirt of her dres
and fingered her hair to make sure it was combed ove
the bruise that still throbbed intermittently. She too
a steadying breath and walked into the *salon.*

There was an instant pause in the conversation as th
people there looked at her; she had never felt so sel
conscious in her life. Zonar stood at the side of hi
brother, and there on one of the velvet couches sat
slender woman with shining hair to the shoulders of
jewel-green evening dress. She wore diamonds with
fire at the heart of them; in her earlobes, around he
honeyed throat, and upon her hand. Beside her on th
couch sat Aleko in his very best suit; he grinned at Iri
but made no attempt to leave the side of his aunt.

'Let me introduce you, Miss Ardath,' Zonar ap
proached her and she felt his firm grip on her elbow
'first to my sister-in-law Fenella, the most beautifu
woman I know.'

Fenella smiled and shook her head at him in affe
tionate reproof. 'It's just as well for you, brother-in-law
that Lion knows that I don't take you seriously.'

'What a pity,' Zonar drawled, 'when I mean ever
word. You look wonderful, Fenny. I hope Lion know
how lucky he is.'

'Don't concern yourself with my luck.' Cigar smok
eddied from the nostrils of the bold Greek nose of Lio
Mavrakis, and it took Iris's breath away when she me
the man's eyes. She had expected them to be dark lik
Zonar's, but instead they were a tiger-amber under th
slashing black eyebrows, the only handsome feature
the strong, swarthy face that showed the marks of

ard life; of a man who had clawed his way out of the arsh back streets of Greece, using hands, wits and a uthless determination. He held Iris's gaze as he drew n the smoke of his cigar appreciatively.

'Iris, eh? Messenger of the gods,' he drawled.

She blushed, and then felt Zonar's fingers tighten pon her arm. 'The Greek gods,' he said. 'Fenny, meet ny son's governess, who has always lived very sedately n a convent until she came to us.'

'I'm so pleased to know you. What a very pretty ame you have; it matches your eyes.' Fenny smiled, er own eyes as blue as speckless skies, unshadowed ow, though Zonar had hinted that she had not had an asy time with the tall, hard-muscled Greek who looked s tough as his wife was tender.

'Now come and greet me,' Lion ordered. 'I'm unccustomed to meeting convent girls, and I'm informed y that young nephew of mine that you are going to ake the veil. Is it a fact?'

He held his gaze intently on her face, with those eyes hat plucked away her composure as if it were a flimsy arment. Iris wanted to edge closer to Zonar, but he ad moved away to the drinks table and left her unrotected. Then, quite unexpectedly, Lion Mavrakis niled and it was a smile of the most unexpected charm, that instantly she understood why a graceful gentle irl like Fenella had fallen in love with him.

'Don't be scared of me,' he said. 'In certain ways I n less dangerous than that good-looking brother of ine; and you have now been living in his house for everal weeks. You are good friends with Aleko, eh?'

'Yes, we get along fine, Mr Mavrakis.' Her own smile as still a little shy, for in several ways he seemed more reign, more Greek than Zonar, who had been fortu-

nate enough to receive a better education which th
older brother had provided. In travelling for the Ma
rakis Corporation he had mixed with sophisticate
people and picked up some of their ways . . . in the yea
of his widowhood Zonar had played the game of lov
but Lion had won it.

Iris's glance went to the equally tall figure who wa
pouring champagne into fluted wine glasses, and sh
felt a sudden stab of compassion for him. He looke
somehow lonely standing over there and she couldn
help wondering why he hadn't invited Colette to joi
the dinner party.

'I know your tipple, Fenny.' His eyes seemed to care
her fair-skinned face. 'I add a third of pure orang
juice to your champagne, eh?'

'Please.' She smiled at him, and then glanced dow
at Aleko, who was absorbed in a large illustrated boo
about dinosaurs and other extinct monsters. 'Alek
grows more like you, Zonar, each time I see him. He'
be the image of you when he grows up.'

'There is just a little of his mother in him.' Zon
came across the room with a tray of filled glasses.
see it now and then. Come, we must drink a toast, for
isn't often these days that we manage to get together.'

'Am I having champagne as well, Papa?' Alek
smiled up at Zonar, and when the dark eyes narrowe
slightly Iris knew that her employer was seeing th
vagrant resemblance to his wife in the boy.

'Champagne and orange juice like your aunt's, an
the same for Miss Ardath.' The dark eyes were su
denly holding Iris's and she felt the cool smoothness
the wine glass he placed in her hand. For the space of
heartbeat she couldn't seem to take her gaze from h
lean face, then he had strolled to where his broth

tood, framed by the long windows that opened on to a errace above the cliffs.

Lion raised his glass. '*Chairete*,' he said. 'Happiness sn't easy to find, but it's well worth the search. *Evty-heite*.'

They drank from their glasses, and Fenny invited ris to sit at the other side of her. The crêpe-de-chine kirt fluttered delicately around her as she sat down n the couch; she felt a little more at ease with these eople but remained uneasy about herself. The dress itted her body, but not the person she had planned ll her life to be. Safe inside the convent it had been asy enough to follow a chosen path, but now she felt ost and vulnerable, and unsure of happiness. If love vas happiness, then she was going to be denied and he knew it.

'Such a pretty dress,' Fenny commented. 'Did you uy it locally? I know there are some very good shops n town.'

'Mr Mavrakis bought it for me.'

'I see—and understand.' Fenny smiled knowingly. He didn't much care for your plain convent wear, is hat it?'

'He was considerably rude about my convent wear,' ris admitted.

Fenny looked amused and glanced over to where the reek brothers were in conversation. 'My husband and onar are renowned for their candour; do you think ney look alike?'

'Yes,' Iris said at once, 'when they smile.'

'I know exactly what you mean.' Fenny had her wine lass clasped between her hands and her eyes had a nouldering blue look as they dwelt upon her husband. Charm is released in Lion when he smiles, but when he looks stern he rather frightens people. He used t frighten me, but that was a long time ago. Does Zona frighten you, Iris?'

The question filtered through Iris's mind ... ther were degrees of being frightened by a man and sh knew (oh God, she knew) that Zonar could never exer his power to hurt and shame a woman. She heard her self say quietly: 'He's a gentleman.'

'Yes,' Fenny agreed. 'Lion knows it and he's prou of the way Zonar has turned out. It was a struggle fo him financially putting his two brothers throug school, but somehow he achieved it; but there's an in herent kindness in Zonar, a kind of understanding tha makes of him a very good friend when one is in troubl I had some trouble, you know, and Zonar pulled m through it. I'll always be grateful to him for lendin me his broad shoulder to lean on. Tell me——'

Fenny hesitated, her eyes fixed upon Iris. 'You prob ably know of his friendship with a girl at the hotel– Colette, I believe he called her. She was there when w had tea, after he took Lion on a tour of the Monarch. very fashionable type of girl, a model from Paris. Yo have met her?'

'Yes, I know her.' Iris could guess what Fenny wante to ask.

'Do you think he's serious about her?' Fenny aske keeping her voice low.

'I don't really know——' Iris edged away from th question. 'I'm only the governess and it isn't my plac to make suppositions about Mr Mavrakis. He sees Co ette quite frequently; I believe she amuses him, and sh is very attractive.'

Fenny frowned slightly. 'Obviously attractive,' sh agreed. 'The kind who would like to marry a man wit money and position, and someone like Zonar should be married just for himself. He needs to be loved, and superficial people don't know the meaning of the word! That girl at the hotel is superficial, isn't she? You've seen that for yourself—I can see it in your eyes as I speak of her.'

Iris dropped her gaze to the wine glass in her hand. 'It isn't for me to have an opinion, Mrs Mavrakis.'

'Isn't it?' Fenny touched her hand. 'Do call me Fenny; all my friends do so, and I'd like us to be friends. Is it true that you're only taking leave of absence from the convent?'

'Yes.'

'It's an immense step to take. I don't know that I'd have the strength for it.' Fenny's gaze went across the room to her husband and Iris saw again the smoulder of love in the wide eyes that were so beautifully set in the otherwise quiet face. Yes, the glamour of loving and being loved very ardently lay in this woman's lovely eyes; an excitement clung to her graceful shape: whatever her nightmare had been it had turned into a dream which enraptured her. That she loved Lion ... adored him, was apparent to anyone who looked at her, and Iris found herself looking at Zonar and searching his face. Fenny was so different from the portrait of Zonar's young dead wife in the ikon-frame which always stood on the night table beside Aleko's bed. She had been as dark-haired as Fenny was fair. Her eyes had been as brown as Fenny's were blue. She had been as Greek as the Mavrakis brothers.

With an abrupt little laugh Zonar said to Fenny: 'This husband of yours is a great deal more charming than he used to be. Have you been giving him lessons?'

Fenny smiled, and Lion answered for her. '*Ne*, brother, we learn together about happiness. It's the being together; it's as simple as that.'

'I'm impressed.' Zonar quirked an eyebrow. 'Have you been sailing on the black-sailed *caique* just lately?'

'Across to Crete a while back. The going was perfect and I reeled in a small shark.'

'A shark?' Aleko glanced up with quick interest. 'Did he put up a fight, *thios*?'

'You can bet he did, Aleko *mou*.' Lion studied the boy. 'You must come and stay with us soon, young man. I'll teach you how to fish the Aegean; would you like that?'

Aleko nodded, then put a hand to his forehead and rubbed it. He looked rather pale, Iris noticed with concern, and there were little shadows under his eyes. He had probably been playing in the sunshine and had tired himself, but she didn't like to suggest to Zonar that the boy ought to go to bed ... she would sound like a spoilsport.

They went in to dine, in the room with the soaring windows and high ceiling, which somehow trapped the sound of the sea. The walls were clad in honey-coloured wood and adorned by a collection of country-life prints. A pendant lamp hung above the oval-shaped table set round with shellback chairs, the light shining down warmly on the crystalware, the lace place mats and roses cut from the garden.

'This all looks very nice.' Fenny smiled appreciatively as she settled into her chair. 'This is a most attractive house, Zonar. How lucky you were to find it.'

'House and governess,' Lion remarked, casting

faintly quizzical look at Iris. 'Is there a chance of a purchase?'

'Of house or governess?' Zonar enquired, his teeth snapping a bread stick.

'Which would you prefer, brother?'

'Behave yourselves, you two,' Fenny ordered. 'Iris isn't accustomed to the tavern talk of Greek men when they get together.'

'Really, *agape mou*?' Lion reached out and swung the diamond-drop in his wife's earlobe; it glittered and gleamed like a small flame. 'I don't imagine she has lived with my brother without finding out that he has at times a healthy disrespect for the proprieties.'

'Iris doesn't exactly—well, you know.' Fenny cast a look at Aleko, who sat beside his father a little too quietly for Iris's peace of mind.

'Of course I know.' Lion's eyes through his lashes were a slumbrous shade of gold. 'I've only to look at the girl.'

'Then stop being so wicked!'

'You knew I was wicked when you stole me at the altar,' he mocked, bringing into Fenny's cheeks a deep blush. 'You see that, Zonar! I can still make her do it!'

Zonar smiled across the table into Fenny's eyes. 'If Lion doesn't know yet that he married an angel in disguise, then he'll never know it, will he?'

'I'm no angel,' she rejoined. 'He was so mad he nearly broke my neck—I look back and wonder how I had nerve to do what I did. I guess I was young and idiotically romantic about him. He made other men seem so tame.'

'I hope, wife, that I still do!' Lion exclaimed.

'You do darling,' she said demurely, 'except when Zonar's in the same room with you.'

At any other time Iris would have been intrigued, if a little perplexed, by this recounting of family history, but she was watching Aleko. When a dish of stewed snails, dressed with tomatoes and peperoni, was brought in for Lion and the whiff of garlic caught in the boy's nostrils, he suddenly retched and in an instant Iris was upon her feet and attending to him with a table napkin. His face was now like chalk and he was hunched over, holding his stomach.

'What have you been eating?' Zonar demanded.

'Mussels,' he whimpered. 'At a stall down on the harbour——'

'By the gods!' Zonar swept his son up into his arms. 'Milk! He'll guzzle it until it comes out of his ears! In the meantie, Iris, get on the phone to that doctor who came to see you. Tell him what the little devil's been eating, and be quick!'

'Can I do anything?' Lion was upon his feet, with Fenny clutching his sleeve and looking very concerned.

'Papa——' Aleko was moaning in a very forlorn way. 'I've ever such a pain——'

'You'll have it on your backside tomorrow.' Zonar shook his head in answer to Lion, then marched away in the direction of the kitchen. Iris at the telephone table dialling the doctor's number heard him say to the boy: 'You'll be afloat in milk before I've done with you. What have I told you about eating at fish stalls?'

'You did—you ate octopus.'

'I was a street urchin with a tough stomach lining——' The deep voice faded away, and Iris could feel the nerves contracting inside her own stomach as she explained the situation to the doctor, who very luckily was at home and able to attend on Aleko immediately.

She sighed as she cradled the phone. Someone

touched her on the shoulder and she turned and found Lion towering over her. 'Drink this—you look as pale as that boy.' A glass was placed in her hand and she automatically drank the cognac he had poured.

'Not to worry,' he urged. 'The doctor is on his way and Zonar is very capable in a crisis—better than I am, as a matter of fact.'

'It's my fault,' she said shakily. 'I should have gone straight to the hotel this afternoon, but I—I went down on the beach instead a-and fell asleep there ...'

Suddenly a ragged sob choked her, and the next instant Lion had wrapped an arm about her and pulled her to his shoulder. She heard him say something in Greek to his wife, but all she really knew was an uprising of pure misery ... the tears welled and for a minute or so she couldn't control them. A large handkerchief found its way into her hand and she buried her face in it, breathing the cigar smoke that reminded her of Zonar.

'Aleko will be all right,' Fenny assured her. 'You mustn't upset yourself like this or you'll be needing the doctor.'

'I—I'm all right now.' Iris wiped away her tears and had herself in control again. She drew away from Lion and glanced along the passageway leading to the kitchen. 'I want to go and see if Aleko is all right—do you think I might?'

'Go!' Lion spoke decisively. 'Better for you to be with him than worrying your heart out. Hurry along, Fenny and I will wait for the doctor to arrive.'

CHAPTER EIGHT

IRIS hurried towards the kitchen, her legs feeling weak at the knees and a fluttery feeling in her stomach. She could barely forgive herself for not realising that if Aleko was left alone with another boy, the pair of them would get into some kind of mischief.

She pushed open the kitchen door, then gave a gasp as someone came out and almost knocked her off her feet. She glanced up wildly into the swarthy face of Achille, an instant tide of repulsion sweeping over her.

'Mind your step, governess, or you'll be knocking yourself out again.'

'Move out of my way——'

But he stood there taunting her with his eyes. 'So you didn't drown, eh?'

'Is that what you hoped would happen?' Iris could hardly bear it that his mouth had crushed hers, that his hands had roamed over her ... that knocked out cold she had been unable to defend herself against him. She felt as nauseated as little Aleko.

'Let me pass!'

'The forfeit is a kiss.' He brought his face down to hers, and as the hate surged in her Iris tensed her fingernails and clawed him as wilfully as a tormented cat.

'Bitch!' His hand sprang to his skinned cheek. 'You only got what you asked for, you little madam. I suppose if it had been the boss you'd have been willing enough——'

'You're lucky you still have your job,' she cut in.

'Why, haven't you gone blabbing to him about me, elling him how a man dared to put his arms around our sacred little figure?' Achille peered down at her, hen gave an incredulous look. 'You don't imagine I ook advantage of you while you were out cold, do you? like my women warm and willing and in their senses. 'm no saint, governess, but I'm not that abominable!'

He marched off with the words and Iris swayed where he stood and caught at the frame of the door, absorbng the shock of relief. She hadn't been entirely sure, or life in a convent did make for a certain innocence bout certain facts of life. Oh, what a blessed weight ff her heart ... yes, she realised, off her heart!

She took a deep breath and composed herself; she vas about to face Zonar's anger at her, and concern for is son.

She entered the kitchen where she found a wanooking Aleko nestled in his father's arms. 'He's been as ck as a newt,' Zonar informed her, and he gave her t the same time a very intent look. 'It seems he and his other boy went down into town and guzzled half a ail of ice-cream between them, a bag of doughnuts, nd then a dish of mussels. It isn't food poisoning, just ure greed.'

'It's all my fault,' she said contritely. 'Had I gone raight to the Monarch and collected him, this ouldn't have happened.'

'True,' he agreed. 'Cook has made some coffee; you ok as if you could do with a cup.'

They were drinking it when the doctor arrived. fter examining Aleko he agreed with Zonar that the y had suffered a bilious attack and would be fine ain after a night's sleep. The doctor departed, the boy was put to bed, and the four shaken adults settled down to a belated supper.

'Children!' Lion exclaimed. 'Are they worth it?'

Fenny glanced up at him, curled against his knee on a velvet hassock, the glimmering skirt of her gown like a sea of green around her slender figure. 'You know they are,' she said softly. 'You wouldn't be withou that child, would you, Zonar?'

'I've lived for him.' Zonar lounged in his armchai rather broodingly, eyelids weighted as cheroot smok eddied about his dark head.

'Isn't it about time you started living for yoursel old man?' Lion's hand was curled about Fenny's shoul der, and Iris on the edge of the family group had th feeling she ought to say goodnight and quietly leav them to their discussion. Yet she lingered a momen more, curious about Zonar's reply to his brother's ques tion. Would he mention Colette? Would he say that h had decided to take a wife ... that he was lonely an this was underlined for him seeing Fenny and Lion together, and so right in their togetherness?

'You aren't getting any younger,' Lion added. 'I would be good for the boy to have a mother, and fo you to have a loving companionship. Ah, I know ther are young women with whom you pass the tim brother, but time has a way of slipping through th fingers and Aleko will be a young man while you wi be an old one. Think on it.'

'I have been thinking about it.' Zonar blew cheroo smoke at the ceiling; it made patterns in the air a through her lashes Iris scanned his face and saw th moodiness in his eyes. 'I do have a wish to re-marry, bu I have not found the right moment for my proposal. I has been a long time since I proposed to a girl.'

'Don't tell me you're afraid of a refusal?' Lion scoffed. 'You have presence and you have position; what more could a girl want?'

'There are strange things that girls want.' Zonar rose to his feet and went to the long windows, where he gazed out across the terrace at the sky. 'By the gods, so many stars! The night is so alive with them, it's almost frightening. Like shards of silver they pierce the sky in every direction; the sea beneath them is calm and clear. My mind isn't. I'm afraid to speak it at the present time.'

'You were never afraid of things, Zonar.'

He turned so his back was to the window and he gave Fenny a quizzical smile. 'Not the things that I can see, lovely lady.'

'Don't you see love when you look at this girl?' she asked quietly.

'I desire love when I look at this girl,' he murmured. 'But I ask myself does she know the meaning of love.'

Iris knew that he had to be speaking of Colette and it was then that she decided to go to bed. She rose quietly from her chair, and then jarred the little chinoiserie table beside it, attracting Zonar's attention to herself.

'Where are you going?' he demanded.

'I'm tired, *kyrie*. I wish to go to bed.'

His eyes swept her face, a little pale and pensive in the monk-like frame of her hair. Unaware she must have pushed her hair away from her temple, for suddenly with a frown he was striding across to her. 'How did you come by this?' He touched a finger to the abrasion she had tried to hide from him. 'Knocked out cold on the beach while you were playing about with my chauffeur?'

Her heart thumped; so he had heard what Achille had said to her outside the kitchen door, which hadn't been completely closed, she remembered. His dark gaze dominated her, a scornful anger burning at their centres. 'I thought puritans had integrity and a sense of duty,' he said sarcastically. 'What became of yours. eh?'

'I'm too tired——' She swayed away from him. 'I've said I'm sorry about Aleko——'

'Playing around with my driver while that boy was running loose and making himself sick——' The flames flared in Zonar's eyes and suddenly he swung his hand as if to strike her. She cried out, then was running from him, across the room, out of the door and across the hall to the stairs. He was coming after her when Lion thundered his name. Iris didn't look back but ran upstairs as fast as her feet would carry her; when she reached her room she rushed inside, flung the door shut behind her and stood there panting for breath.

She would leave the villa first thing in the morning. There was nothing left to stay for . . . the time had come to return to St Claire's.

Suddenly there was a knock on her door and she shivered in conjunction with it. 'It's me, Fenny,' called a voice.

Iris hesitated, then turned to open the door. Fenny stood there with a concerned look on her face. 'Lion sent me up to make sure you're all right—are you?'

'Yes.' Iris swallowed as if to ease the lump in her throat. 'Zonar was justifiably angry. I've broken his trust in me and I've decided to leave Tormont in the morning.'

'I see.' Fenny didn't attempt to argue with her.

You're going back to the convent, is that it? You've lecided to take your vows?'

'Yes.'

'Disregarding the fact that you're head over heels in ove with Zonar?'

The heart shook inside Iris, and her hand climbed o the cross at her throat as if seeking its support. Her yes were tormented and with a murmur of sympathy 'enny turned away. 'I'll tell the men you're all right. won't mention that you're leaving, but I warn you that onar won't leave it at that. The Mavrakis men are bstinate devils and he won't find another governess ike you.'

'Like me?' Iris drew a shaky breath. 'He believes I've een having a good time with his chauffeur; I was down n the beach with Achille, but he followed me there nd tried to make love to me. I fought him off and hit ny head on a stone. He left me lying there and luckily he incoming tide brought me to my senses.'

'Zonar has to be told this,' Fenny exclaimed. 'Let ne——'

'No, please!' Iris had made up her mind to leave; she ouldn't stay if Zonar was making plans to marry Colette. What she felt went deeper than jealousy. She ad to go as far away from him as possible; she had to ind sanctuary from her own feelings and the state of race that excluded all desire for a man.

'Let him think what he does think,' she pleaded. 'He nustn't come to the convent—from now on he mustn't ome near me!'

'Oh, my dear!' Fenny shook her head and walked way, her green gown glimmering until she melted into he shadows at the far end of the gallery where it turned o meet the stairs. Like a lovely apparition she was gone, seeking the warmth and reassurance of the man who loved her. Iris retreated into her room, which felt cold and lonely ... cold like the chapel at St Clare's where she must pray to forget the face and form of Zonar Mavrakis, until she could stand alone again, secure in her self-imposed aloneness.

The clock ticked and she stared at the face of it. If only she could go tonight and get it over with! Perhaps she could? The night porter knew her at the Monarch and he could phone for a cab to take her to the station where she might be lucky enough to catch the midnight express to London. From there she could easily catch a train into Waltham.

She began to pack the bag she had brought with her, bundling in the plain bits of clothing she hadn't worn since Zonar had bought her the new clothes. She took off the crêpe-de-chine dress and hung it back in the closet, stroking the soft skirt he had stroked before closing the door on the finery she wouldn't see or wear again. She dressed in a plain blouse and skirt and put on her navy-blue coat.

Perhaps Zonar and his family would still be talking in the *salon* and with luck she would manage to slip out of the house without being seen. She glanced around the bedroom to make sure everything was neat and tidy; she would never sleep in such a room again, waking to sunlight through the oval windows and to the sound of the sea and the gulls on the cliffs. She would have liked to kiss Aleko goodbye, but time was ticking away and she must leave now, quickly and quietly.

The long sweep of stairs to the hall were carpeted so she made no sound going down them; her heart seemed to come into her throat as she crossed the hall to the

ont door. Carefully she opened it and the next mo-
ıent was outside and closing it with equal care behind
er. The night air was blowing up from the sea as she
ıade her way along the drive to the road.

She drew her coat around her, aware that most of the
ɔldness was inside her body. The image of the *salon*
as painfully clear in her mind, the pattern on the
ırpet, the velvety couches, the softly shaded lights
laying in and out of dark eyes.

What were they discussing now . . . reliving memories
f Greece perhaps, when the brother were boys and still
› make a success of their lives? She had liked Fenny
ıd after the initial feeling of intimidation had dis-
ɔvered that Lion Mavrakis was less fierce than he
ɔoked. Love had mellowed him, but what kind of
ɔve did Zonar expect from his marriage, if it took
lace?

Iris sighed as she traversed the winding road that led
ɔwn towards the glimmering light of the Monarch
lotel. She glanced up at the sky and saw the silver
aws of the stars etched into the silent sensuous velvet
ıat stretched above the dark countryside and the sea.
ıe walked on mutely, her hair faintly luminous in
ıe starlight. When she reached the hotel and walked
ıto the foyer the porter stared at her in amazement.

'You, miss? What are you doing out so late?'

'I have to catch a train to London. Could you phone
cab for me?' She opened her purse and extracted
ɔme money; he shook his head, but she laid it on his
esk. 'Please!'

'Bad news, miss?' He gave her wan face a concerned
ɔok.

'Something like that.' That coldness inside her made
er shiver again.

He nodded and began to dial a number. 'Turned bit colder, has it? Perhaps we're due for a spot of ra —gardens could do with it after the dry spell. Ah, that you, Ray? Got a cab you can send up to t Monarch? I have a young lady here who has to cat a train to London. Right-o. Ten minutes to wait.'

The porter smiled at Iris. 'The cab won't be lo coming for you. Why don't you sit down and take t weight off your feet?'

But she felt restless and wandered across the softly foyer to one of the showcases in which evening purs scarves and costume jewellery were displayed. It w late, but a few of the guests still sat about in t lounge; Iris caught the murmur of their voices as s gazed at a jewelled butterfly pinned against white sati

Isle of butterflies, she thought, bright and gauzy the air, flying by scent alone to the mates they loved the wing. Free ... free to love while she was on her w back to the stone walls and the solemn vows th turned love into a forbidden thing.

She swung round from the showcase and blocki her path was a tall figure wearing a suede car-coat, t collar up about his neck. She caught her breath wh she realised who it was; almost without knowing it s half raised a hand as if to ward him off.

'Where do you think you're going?' he demanded.

'To the convent——' Her heart was hammering. 'Y can't stop me.'

'I'd take you if I really believed that you want to back to the place.'

'Of course I want to go—I have to go!'

'What makes you think so?' He touched the da mole on the left side of his jaw; her eyes were fixed up it. 'Do you think I bear the mark of the devil?'

'There are times when you—you behave like a devil.'
he began to back away from him until with a gasp
he came to a halt against one of the foyer columns of
ool marble. She stood there tensely as he towered
ver her, his gaze pinning her even as he pressed a hard
eg against her and threatened her with his body.

'Is this one of them?' he drawled softly. 'Are you run-
ing away from me, or are you so desperately eager to
e chaste that you're taking the midnight train?'

'I have to go back,' she repeated. 'I have to do it.'

'Over my dead body, you little fool!'

Her own body seemed to weaken and swiftly he en-
ircled her with his arms and swung her off her feet. He
trode out into the night with her, past the desk where
he porter watched speechlessly. A rake of dark hair lay
cross Zonar's forehead and his eyes were dangerous ...
s a tiger's might be if any creature attempted to take
is prey.

'You're going home,' he told her, 'but with me.'

Her face was half hidden in the collar of his coat
nd warmth had come back inside her. Aggressively
nd yet with a certain gentleness he placed her inside
is Jaguar; he stroked his fingers down her cheek and
he could see his eyes smouldering in the soft light
rom above the car doors. Her breath caught in her
hroat and she wanted that look to stay in his eyes, never
change.

'So Fenny told you what I meant to do?' she sighed.

'I know Fenny; I saw a look in her eyes that made me
orry her until she told me. I guessed then what you
ould do, come down to the hotel for a cab and catch
he midnight train if you could. I knew that if you had
run away from me without daring to see me, it was
ecause you couldn't trust your feelings any more.'

He walked round to the driver's door and climbe into the car beside her. His hand must have been un steady because he had to try twice before the engin leapt to life and they sped up the incline on to th road. She expected Zonar to turn left towards the vill but instead he took the right turning down to th harbour.

'I want you to myself a little longer,' he said. 'Such night! So many stars—I feel as if they are dancing i my blood.'

Iris watched the bold outline of his profile as the drove along beside the rambling harbour wall whe intermittent lights were trapped softly in the wate They drove past shadowy lanes and old narrow hous with tiny-paned windows. Dark sheets of ivy mantle the curving walls of all that remained of an ancie castle; the headlights broke open the darkness as the sped along, revealing and then concealing the crooke trees and sprawling hedgerows. A rabbit darted into th road and missed their wheels by the stub of its tail an she wondered if Zonar would have stopped had th rabbit been less quick.

'It isn't always possible to stop ourselves.' He turne his head to look briefly at her and she saw the glimm of his teeth.

Through the open windows of the car she caught th aroma of horses and realised they were on the Honeyto road where the stables were; where she hadn't dared t learn how to ride because it would have been impossib to go on riding when she took her vows.

A few yards further along the road they turned pa the old mill and drove upon the humpbacked litt bridge where a stream meandered. Zonar stopped th car and sat there with an arm upon the wheel, starin a moment through the windshield. Iris could smell honeysuckle, wafting in through the windows on the soft night air. Strange how the coldness had gone out of the night.

'You belong to me.' Zonar turned to her and captured her hands, holding them between his own so she felt the pressure of the marriage rings, symbols of the love he had felt and shared with a girl of his own. 'You belong in my arms and I won't let you give yourself—all the slim sweetness of you—to that cold stony place. I can't! I won't! Do you hear me?'

'Yes, you've always had a voice that could carry across a courtyard.' She looked at him with a certain demureness. 'You were shouting at me an hour ago because you thought I was playing around with your driver. You know that isn't true, don't you?'

'Yes—I'll break his damned neck for him!'

'That's why I didn't dare to say anything.'

'Then you know how I feel about you?'

'I—I think you might want me because you can't have——'

'Colette?'

Iris shook her head and felt the painful tightening of his hands.

'Who the devil do you mean?'

'Fenny. I feel sure you love her——'

'I love her madly. She's the kindest and most gracious girl in the world. I give thanks that she has made my brother a happy man. I wouldn't wish for a nicer sister-in-law.' Suddenly Zonar's arms were around Iris and he was pulling her to him, close inside his coat to his warm chest. 'I love Fenny as a sister, my little fool. I love you—I love you with a mad longing I haven't felt since I was a youth. I see you and I want you. I touch you and

I could eat you. I'll take you here and now if it will prove to you that you aren't one of these passionless women who can devote themselves to righteous causes and get their satisfaction out of it. In your heart you want me as much as I want you—come, admit it! I demand that you admit it!'

Her upraised face was slightly grave, but into his had come a look that bordered on savagery, as if the primitive Greek in him was taking over from the suave man of business. There was a tremor in his arms and he was breathing quickly through tensed nostrils.

'I'm so hungry for you, girl. I've been so alone in my heart, then you walked into that room at the convent and looked at me as you are looking now—as if you want to run and stay at one and the same time. Stay with me, Iris. Don't leave me alone to go to the devil—by the gods, if you need a good cause, then take me on.'

He pressed his face down against hers and she felt the uneven drag of his breath against her skin. This was Zonar, the tall Greek who had come into her life and turned her aside from the destiny she would have followed without question had she never met him.

'Aleko needs you as well,' he whispered. 'Aren't the pair of us a good enough cause for your devotion?'

Her hand stole up his strong back to the nape of his neck and she felt the tremor that ran through him. Had Reverend Mother known all along that she would fail the test that made women strong enough to cast a man's love and need out of their lives? Iris knew she had failed, but the radiance that was spreading inside her told her that she had also won.

She moved her lips against Zonar's cheek and heard him give a soft groan. 'Ah, darling, darling, don't leave me to go back to that place!'

She knew he wasn't a man who ever pleaded, and it moved her that she should be the one to make him plead. 'It's all right, *kyrie,* I want to stay with you—I hated having to leave you, but I thought——'

'There's no one but you.' He kissed her eyes, her lips, her throat. 'No one since the day we met. You'll marry me?'

'If you want me, sir.'

'Doesn't it feel like it?' He laughed softly and stroked her hair. 'Say my name, Iris.'

'Dearest Zonar.'

'Say again that you love me, Iris.'

'I love you with all my heart.'

'And you'll abide with me?'

'All my days, *kyrie.*'

'And all your nights?'

She was smiling as she met the warmth and wanting of his kiss. She held him as he held her, with an eager passion for all they would share in the communion of marriage.

'Go forth,' Reverend Mother had said, 'and find out to which world you belong.'

Iris knew that she belonged to Zonar Mavrakis ... and it felt wonderful.